Finding the

good

rough the

Rain

anthology

Indignor House
Fall 2023

anthology

Finding the Good through the Rain

First Edition

ISBN 978-1-953278-48-7 Hard Back
ISBN 978-1-953278-49-4 Soft Back
ISBN 978-1-953278-50-0 E-Book

This is a work of fiction. The characters are both actual and fictitious. With the exception of verified historical events and persons, all incidents, descriptions, dialogue and opinions expressed are the products of the author's imagination and are not to be construed as real.

Published by

INDIGNOR
HOUSE

Chesapeake, VA 23322
www.indignorhouse.com

Cover Design: Indignor House

Contents

An Introduction 1
Lynn Yvonne Moon

Growing Up Aspie 3
Lynn Yvonne Moon

A Tumbleweed and a Story 7
Jonathan Michael Stroh

ASPIC 21
Anaissa Ali

Beautiful Wreckage 27
Valerie Dawn

Birds 39
Elizabeth Elder

Bridge 45
D.M. Clemens

Eden's Rain 57
Samuel G. Tooma

Gears and Flowers 77
Tai An Zhou

Getting Out 91
Bruce Neuburger

Into the Light 107
Jerry Aveta

It Was Worth It 123
Onyx Rebel

Knitting in the Dark 131
Morna Gersho

Contents - Continued

Knitting in the Dark ... 131
Morna Gersho

Last Legs ... 139
Kevin Hopson

Mama Luisa ... 145
Thomas Bell

Rainy Day Memories ... 159
Roger Guffey

Shy Boy ... 167
Frank Shima

Spiraling ... 177
Tia Shanklin

The Glitch ... 185
Arthur M. Doweyko

The Prodigal Cousin ... 205
Gary Girzadas

The Puddle and The Ghost ... 221
Lady Beth

The Undead FriendZone ... 233
Tyler Tarter

Ticket to Abbeville ... 245
Kristine K. McCraw

Timothy's Birth Day ... 257
Mary Bendickson

Biographies ... 267

An Introduction

Rain … water … the purifier of life. We cannot live without it. Our bodies are mostly water. The world is over seventy percent water. And … there's about 37.5 million-billion gallons floating around in our atmosphere. Interesting little tidbits.

For this year's anthology, we wanted to find the beauty behind the ugly, the happiness blended in with the sadness, the light within hidden inside the shadows. And our authors did not let us down.

Life's lessons can be harsh. Experiencing a death, living through a catastrophe, or the self-imposed prisons we create for ourselves, all center around the status life has handed us.

Through the endowment of speech, humans communicate their thoughts, emotions, and hope. I believe that it is through *hope,* we often find our rainbows. What if we started following these colors and see where they lead?

My experiences in life have taught me that we are the same everywhere. No matter the color of our skin, the gender of our cells, the tint of our eyes, or the sound of our voice, we are the same. We experience pain, happiness, excitement, hope, fear … must I continue? So I will ask this question … why do we fight?

Does greed determine who we are? Do we have to have more *stuff* than our neighbors? If we lived in a single tribe, would we make our citizens starve or sleep in the cold? Then why do we do it now?

Perhaps it is because not everyone can find the good through the rain.

"Enjoy the little things in life, for one day you may look back and realize they were the big things." Robert Brault

What are the little things compared to the big? Our children find wonder in a newly bloomed flower or a ripe tomato or the sun's rays. Why can't we? Why do we lose that ability as we age?

"Life is not a problem to be solved, but a reality to be experienced."

Soren Kierkegaard

If we walk through life enjoying the experiences, would our problems turn into puzzles we could solve? And do we not enjoy the pieces of a puzzle with family and friends? If the answer is yes, maybe the stories in this anthology will touch your heart as they did mine.

As you travel through the pages, look deep into your soul and ask yourself a few of these questions. Perhaps, we can bring a little good into your life too.

Lynn Yvonne Moon
Chief Executive Officer

Growing Up Aspie

Lynn Yvonne Moon

I'm an Aspie. What's an Aspie? Simple answer … anyone diagnosed with Asperger Syndrome – a dot on the line of the autistic scale. The condition was not widely known or accepted until the late 1990's, and by that time, I had already raised four kids and learned to simply tolerate life. Born in the 1950's, the chance of anyone recognizing what was wrong and why I was struggling was indeed a long shot. Instead, they labeled me as retarded and that brand remained with me forever, destroying my marriages and relationships.

Growing up in a mid-size town probably didn't help. With everyone knowing everyone else, the stigma of being different was a constant companion. Or, should I say curse? Retarded, stupid, and troublemaker were few of the nicer nicknames. It wasn't until I reached my mid-thirties that I realized I was something more than just words.

Living a lie that others created made me who I am today. Constantly, I have challenged what others believe I could or could not accomplish. Their skepticism gave me a reason to push myself. Nothing ever comes easy. I just had to try harder than most. But eventually, I shattered through the glass ceiling others had built over me. Now with several higher degrees on my resume, I've learned to accept and work with my autism.

Maybe my story will help others to understand that they too can overcome what stands in their way. Or perhaps I can light a little spark for a mom or dad as they watch their Aspie child struggle.

With that, I tell you that Growing Up Aspie can be a wonderful experience.

Where to search for more information about raising a child with Asperger Syndrome:

https://www.aane.org
https://autismsociety.org
https://www.autism.org.uk

AN INTRODUCTION

A TUMBLEWEED AND A STORY

Jonathan Michael Stroh

Joey Hannah's life peaked when he won his first short story competition. He was seven. His story was published in a Chicago's youth writing competition, sandwiched between a six-year-old champion with his tale, and an eight-year-old champion with her tale. Parents of the six-year-old losers speculated that the father, a best-selling author, had illegally contributed to his son's entry.

Joey's yarn read a little glib to some. Laden with early aughts household imagery (motivational Hallmark signs explaining 'a little dirt never hurt' and chalkboard walls and tacky off-gray futons), the narrative arc slowed near the crest when the monster, his main character, composed entirely of superfluous, niche coffee table books, began tearing the pages from its own form in a distraught, psychological state.

The final poignant scene of a young boy weeping as he noticed the cup rings and beer spills and boot marks like middle-class-scars over his beloved, eccentric, eclectic collections of coffee-table books, probably won him top honors.

Ten years passed. While his dad spent eleven hours a day behind the gray-silver counter of the family-owned delicatessen, folding prosciutto, salami, and pancetta onto Italian loaves, Joey entered forty-one short fiction competitions, winning six and nabbing silver in three. Those concerned agreed, he displayed the promise of a solid, second-tier author. Not a Mount-Rushmore-Atwood or McCarthy-type, of course, but something a little below.

In the starless nights of his childhood, when he buried the memory of his mom and baby brother beneath the detritus of the day, and after a sour goodnight kiss from his dad, he'd curl up in the alcove beneath the windowsill and gaze across the wasteland of streetlights and ponder which stories matter in an as-good-as-infinite universe. Live your life like they're filming a movie, his fifth-grade teacher had said.

"Will my stories matter?" Childish thoughts, really.

"Yo, Joe. I got five on the patio, can you take the four-top at forty-two?"

Joey nodded. A year out of high school, he approached a table of young contemporaries he presumed were students at the university – two gals in dresses and jean jackets – two guys in sweaters with cream collars poking out.

"Hey folks!" Joey stated, his voice instinctively falsetto. "My name's Joey, I'll be taking care of you today. Can I start you off with anything to drink?"

As he scribbled – arnie palmer, arnie palmer, water w lemon, arnie palmer – the gals smiled, friendly. The guys smiled, politely. But in their expressions, he noticed what he'd seen so many times before – *I'm here. You're there.*

"Be quick about my chicken penne alla vodka," one of the guys stated. "I have an interview downtown in ninety."

Joey lugged a dish tub on his hip. He stood at the table and stared.

They left no tip.

He picked up the plate of hardly, touched shrimp scampi and dropped it into the tub. The chicken penne plate on top of that, which revealed a five-dollar bill.

Oh how generous, he thought.

He placed another dish in the tub.

The winds of Lake Michigan tore and bit, whispering ice-cold profanities seven months of the year. A few hours later, his tear ducts felt frozen as he shoulder-opened the door of the hovel. An apartment he shared with Micky Piedmont who was sitting on a tent-chair in their eight-by-eight living room with a porcelain pipe millimeters from his lips.

"Yoooo," Micky whined. "How was work?"

"Work." Joey nodded. "Yeah, same."

"Yeah, same. There's a letter on the counter for yah, Joe."

Joey walked over and picked up the envelope. He read it out loud, "Algonquin Books Raleigh, NC 27710." He tore it open.

> Dear Mr. Hannah,
>
> We regret to inform you, your collection of short stories, *Still Kinda Swimming,* was not the right fit for our company. We hope you find a home for your stor…

He threw the letter in the trash and sat on the tent chair beside Micky.

His roommate read the situation. "Let's medicate." He gestured with the hand holding the pipe. Mickey was wearing jeans and a long sleeve shirt, soil caked under his fingernails, a dirt smear near his right ear. The noxious stench of fertilizer floated through the small room.

"Nah, sorry, Mick. I have class tonight."

"Oh, come on. A little mary-juhwana will get you thinkin circles around these other bookworm folks."

"Eh ..." Joey sighed. *Why does it matter anyway?*

Micky lit the pipe and inhaled, and the white smoke curled off his lips.

Joey stared into the kitchen. *What a dilapidated, brown fridge.*

The winds rattled the window shutters.

"My life's losing momentum," Joey whispered.

The whites of Mickey's eyes resembled a red-networked of spiderwebs. He chuckled. "Someone gave us a shitty role in the sim." He laughed again. "Life cast us as crappy extras in a bad movie."

Joey's mind fell blank. *Fuck all of this. What's class gonna get me?* "Hand me the pipe?"

Joey stared into the bathroom mirror. Red framed his green eyes. Thick, jet-black curls framed his face. He glared at himself, patting the pouch of his belly. He pressed his forehead against the glass and cried.

The following morning, the sky woke in an antagonistic gray. Clouds smothering a ceaseless horizon. The dumpsters in the alleyway soured in the dim light.

"Fitting," Joey whispered.

The lunch rush, amidst olive tapenades and bruschettas and jalapeño poppers galore, Joey found himself staring in reverie at the gloomy sky. The baleful clouds still hovered, but seemed fractured, like a jigsaw puzzle pulled asunder.

Asunder? he thought. *So literary* …

Golden sunrays slipped through the cracks like a break in his reality or perhaps a … sign? A lone dog stared at him from the other side of the street. Thin, sickly, just staring.

"Helloo! Helloo there?" a female voice echoed.

Joey's daydream faded.

A young woman sat at a table with a yellow, legal pad next to the menu. He walked over. Her eyes were blue – a bright, reflecting blue.

Cerulean? No. "How may I help you?"

She was alone.

"Are you expecting anyone?"

She sighed. "No, just taking notes. Would love to order something if that's not too much trouble for a restaurant."

"Notes on a tapas place?" he asked.

"Yeah, for a scene. I'm writing a book. I like to visit the places if that makes sense?" Her eyes resembled an ocean of ideas.

A book? "Yeah." He nodded. "I agree, actually. I write a bit too. How long have you been writing?"

"I entered my first short story competition when I was seven."

Joey's eyes widened. "Did you win?"

She chuckled. "No, I took second, ha-ha. I totally should've won." Her smile brightened. "I actually remember the winner, something about a monster."

He laughed for the first time in days, pulling out a chair. He sat, feeling the eyes of his manager on his neck. She slid her chair back an inch and narrowed her eyes.

"That was me," he replied

"What?" She squinted.

"I wrote that story," he said. "Name's Joey Hannah. Do you still have your copy of the 2008 magazine?"

"No, I don't." She paused and seemed to study him before glancing at the manager who had yet to stop staring at Joey. "A crazy coincidence. I'm Reina." She reached out her hand. "What do you write now?"

"Bad stories. How about you?"

She laughed. "I'm at the university."

"Studying?"

"Just started the MFA program."

He sat back. "A little young. Aren't you around nineteen?"

"Yeah." Reina looked at the silverware. "I skipped two grades in school."

"Wow." He felt inadequate. "Have you written anything recently? I could check it out?"

She laughed and her cheeks flushed. "Something published in Harper's Magazine … that was cool."

Joey stood. "I'm sorry. I shouldn't have sat down." He glanced over his shoulder. "My manager's probably beyond pissed. Is she staring at me?"

She nodded. "Yeah."

"What would you like to order?"

She picked up the menu and sighed. "I'll have a water and the calamari à la plancha and an order of bread … please." She scribbled something on her notepad.

He took a step.

"And Joey? If you want, I'm always looking for fellow writers to chat with."

Joey sat at a too-small desk in a too-small classroom at Olive-Harvey Community College as Professor So-and-So scrawled colors on a whiteboard with their range of possible symbolism.

Wearing a green hoodie and laughing to himself, Joey typed notes on his laptop. He tabbed and searched for the weather and read that snow was possible over the weekend. *Fuck,* he thought, pulling out his phone. He held the scrap of paper with her number on it and typed a short text.

The early spring warmed over the next couple of weeks. That was when Joey first met Reina by Millennium Park. They bought coffee. He asked about her life and they debated over their favorite books

"Grapes of Wrath?" she asked.

"Love it," he replied.

"Then you're weird."

They compared their favorite vegetables and a couple of other things before strolling amongst the tourists. The sky looked clear. From a storefront window, he studied his reflection. He didn't know what protagonist he saw.

They walked along the water's edge and down Navy Pier past the Ferris Wheel. As the sky grew dark, they nibbled on crab wontons.

"Why didn't you go to college?"

Joey looked up. He swallowed too early and it hurt. "It was just my dad and me. When something happened to him, I needed money. I found a job and the tapas place pays good. I take night classes."

"I'm sorry." She rolled an egg roll across her plate with a chopstick. What happened to your mom?"

"Let's wait on that."

"Sure, sure."

They grabbed their fortune cookies and left. Under the streetlights, they kissed. A small one. They bid adieus. He bounced to the train and while waiting, he crumbled the cookie, tossing it in the garbage. He read the thin paper. 'Soon You Will Uncover A Grand Secret.'

He smiled.

For a year, Joey tried to extricate the past from his day-to-day life. But on their anniversary, the rain cannonaded the windows. It was time he had answers from dad.

He borrowed Mickey's truck and drove out of town. He parked beyond the fence that surrounded the tall, gray walls, and walked to the visitor's entrance of Stateville Correctional. They hadn't spoken since the arraignment. In all honesty, they hadn't spoken since his mom died eleven years ago today from a baby and a placental tumor the size of a pomegranate.

The guards searched him before he sat him at a desk with a glass barrier. His father walked out, looking the same as Joey remembered – medium-height, strong-build, bald, and bearded. They picked up the phones. No one spoke for awhile.

"Why?" Joey asked.

His father's beard twitched. "Why what? There was nothing left anyway."

I was left.

His father looked away. "Without your mother …" his voice trailed.

Joey stared at his father. "What happened?"

"Not the fancy story the news spun. I was drunk … and mad. Thought he had said something. Can't remember now if he did or didn't. Maybe he just bumped me. It was dark. And I hit him and …"

Joey stood and left.

Rain pelted the windshield on the drive home. *Boring, bad, horrible, cruel, abominable, odious,* he recited the words in his head.

On the kitchen counter, he found a letter from the University of Chicago. He shredded the envelope opening it.

> Mr. Hannah,
>
> The Admissions Committee has carefully reviewed your application to the University of Chicago. After much consideration, we regret to inform you that we are unable to offer you a place in the class of …

Joey fell into a tent chair. He and Reina had planned a date in Hyde Park. He stood and threw the chair across the room.

Cold drizzled on his walk downtown. Across the street, sniffing at the base of a garbage can was that dog – gray, emaciated, its ribs visible with each breath.

Stupid. He darted across the road. Horns blared and streetwalkers yelled. The dog cut into an alley.

Joey darted around the corner and hit something hard. Stars fizzled across his vision. Two men stared at him. One with a cigar in his hand.

"You punk!" groaned the man who looked like a tree wrapped in leather.

The man picked up Joey by the collar and shoved him against the wall. The back of his head slammed hard on the bricks. He collapsed, his eye catching the corner of a dumpster.

"Reina? I think we should call it quits. What with the last couple of weeks, our lives are pointed along two counter trajectories. I'm fairly certain we're parallel stories. And whoever's writing yours is doing a much better job. I'm so excited to hear about the great things you do …"

Joey sat on the floor mattress and rolled the Smith & Wesson 9 mm Luger between his fingers, feeling the metal like a cold touch, tracing the trigger, pistol grip, barrel, stock. Outside, a storm raged – rain and lightning, thunder. He couldn't write the world anymore. He grabbed the fifth of Daniel's and took a swig. He raised the end of the barrel to his temple. Crying, he fumbled and felt the pistol slip.

BANG!

Nothing but darkness infiltrated his universe. A room and pain and a young man. He felt the side of his head where his ear should have been and instead touched a warm ooze.

A million data points bounced within his ether with a trend-line. He threw the gun into the downpour and ran toward the lake. Drops slapped against his face. His heart pounded and his ear roared.

The gun didn't go off!

It sounded like a bang. Literally, like a bang. Setting the symbolism and the sky, foreshadowing, and a fortune cookie, and a dumb dog – my childhood could be summarized in just a few lines.

"Holy shit," he mouthed.

Joey reached the lakefront trail and hopped on the concrete balustrade, glancing down the slick escarpment and over the roaring water. Violent waves in all their phantasmagoric, ethereal glory, pounded the shoreline.

"Of course you would do this in a storm!" Joey screamed. He laughed and laughed and coughed spit. "You bastard! Who are you? Why tell this story? Why fuck up my life to tell this stupid story!" His tears pooled, but he couldn't cry in the rain. "Answer me! Why does this matter?"

The sky felt like a hyperbole. From the wind and the rain came a mellifluous voice. A soft whisper louder than the tumult. A paradox.

"Joey, I told your story because I cared."

Joey raised his hands to the firmament. "That's not good enough!" His voice broke. "Am I because I am? Or am I because of you?" The wind carried his words through the darkening skies.

"I think because you asked, you just are."

With his one good ear, he could hear only himself.

"You're a storyteller, Joey. You should know. Don't think you're ordinary. From my place behind the camera, you're a hero."

Feeling anger and awe, the goofy feelings of infinitesimal smallness flew through him. Joey thought a silly thought about when no stories mattered. He laughed and cried until the rain slowed.

"What's the level of reality? Imprecise?" he whispered.

On a nondescript, Thursday afternoon in downtown Chicago, suits and pantsuits and ties and sweaters sat at their cubicles on the forty-second floor of the Brooks Building. Most rotated between glancing out windows or staring at spreadsheets.

Yells from the street echoed.

Josie McMinor looked up from her laptop and stood. She glanced out the window. "What's going on?" she asked.

The monster rounded the corner with a shadow the length of the city block. Cars shrieked before plowing into the buildings. Pedestrians threw open the glass doors, clutching their bags.

The monster's foot – a supersized, green hardcover entitled *25 Great Drives in Ireland* crush a yellow Lamborghini like it was a matchbox. The long fingers of the giant composite looked like a collection – Film Art: Introduction, Film Art: Two, Film Art: Three, etc. – and the digits deftly removed patrons from a tapas restaurant before plucking the building from the street like a Lego set, hurling the red-brick establishment into the sky. It splashed into Lake Michigan with a tremendous wave.

An anthropomorphic bookstore. The monster stopped before the Brooks Building, grinning an abundance of cookbook teeth and staring with eyes that read *'Life's One Hundred Photographs That Changed The World.* On its shoulder, atop a book called *Extraordinary Chickens*, sat a young man with green eyes, mountains of jet-black curls, looking at the forty-second floor. He glanced across the lake as he gently patted the coffee table monster book. The two set off south toward Hyde Park and the gothic university.

Lynn's Thoughts …

Jonathan clearly depicts reality in his story of a young writer, trying to survive in a normal world … or what we currently consider as normal. The heartbreak of winning or not winning a writing contest or the deep emotion of defeat when receiving a college rejection letter, all real-life reactions passed through as words scattered across a page.

Joey, our protagonist, lives with an addict in a run-down neighborhood, working as a waiter but still dreaming … however, dreaming of what?

A heart-wrenching story of life's struggles and how we cope. When Joey meets a fellow author, he must endure that love/hate - happy/angry scenario, as he enjoys the days with her, strolling along a street or sipping on hot coffee. Afterall, it was her final story of life that won over his. But in the end, Joey's self-confidence loses. He is unable to accept that this woman is successful and he is not.

The story takes an unexpected turn when Joey tries to end his life only to be recreated as a friend to an actual book monster – one that devours the world where he does not fit. Afterall, if you can't join them, why not eat them? Wait, that is not how that saying goes, is it?

Jonathan does a wonderful job in capturing the pain of accepting our failures and acknowledging defeat. But must it end the same way?

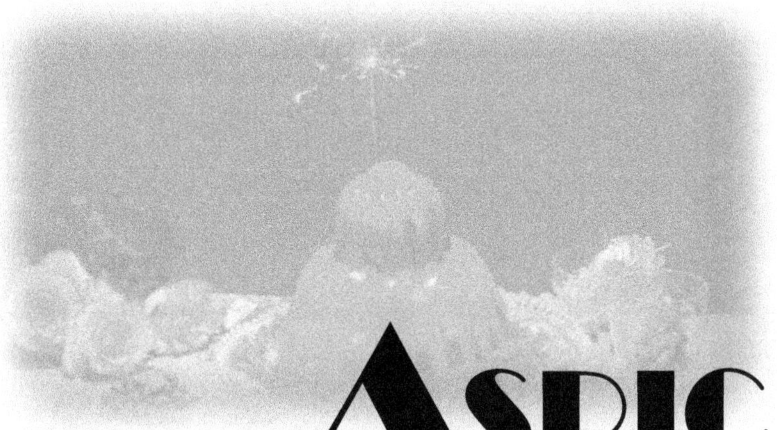

ASPIC

Anaïssa Ali

When love turned into disgust, she felt dirty.

She needed to wash away the shame of allowing it to happen, allowing *him* to enjoy himself at her expense.

When love turned into disgust, she felt dirty.

She needed to wash away the shame of lying in bed next to her ex-boyfriend. They were still living under the same roof ... until she could move out.

When love turned into disgust, she felt dirty.

She needed to wash away the shame from not saying *no.* It was not a *first night* she wanted to remember.

How could she fail to ignore the red flags that waved after only a few weeks? How could she choose to live in denial, projecting herself into an idealized version of a blossoming relationship? But when he said he wished to have a child ···

Everything was happening so fast. Even if they had conceived through love, she had to walk next to his darker side. A soul she was not comfortable living with ... let alone raise a child.

Everything was happening so fast. Yet she knew he was not the man she wanted to spend the rest of her life with.

But she stayed.

Affected by her past and her father, someone not present at her birth, she was broken. A history she did not want for her child ... the feeling of abandonment.

She was holding on to the positive, feeling suffocated when *he* was at home. He was not to be disturbed, and therefore, she looked after their child, alone.

She was holding on to the positive, feeling trapped in a golden cage with no real connection to the outside world.

She had lost her 'joie de vivre.'

She was holding on to the positive, coiling from his sudden outbursts and hateful insults.

After one too many incidents in front of their little prince, it was time to leave. He was not a good role model for their son. She had to leave to provide her son with the chance to live in peace. Two homes in harmony was better than one full of anger.

She was extremely proud for leaving that toxic home. Even with the extra burdens, she was once again allowed to breathe. Maybe they could repair the broken pieces someday and become whole as a family.

As the months passed, she accepted that something was broken inside. Broken for good. She despised being around him. No spark of love existed. No desire for this man. Just an inner voice screaming out for help.

"Make him go … make him go … make him go!"

He refused to accept they were no longer partners and just two people sharing a son. He refused to walk away when all she wanted was for them to focus on being parents.

She saw no other way.

She wrote him a letter. However, he would not take *no* for an answer. She was at peace with *her* decisions. They were the right ones. She stood her ground, leaving him alone at that closed door. A door she would never open. It was, however, the beginning of their undeclared Cold War.

From a distance, he brought turmoil into her life.

But she allowed it to happen.

She could not understand the psychological power he held over her. If he entered this incarnation to be the oppressor, he was playing his role to perfection. Her lack of confidence at being a *good* mother was making her an easy target.

She took it upon herself to ensure her son maintained a relationship with his father. She drove hundreds of kilometers back and forth from Switzerland where he had escaped into exile.

If she endured these exhausting trips like a proud puppet, everything was perfect. Perfect until one day, she tired of the drive. And with the pandemic on the horizon, the opportunity to settle down in Croatia arrived. It was time for her to put herself first.

The undeclared Cold War entered the next phase. A heavy toll landed on her health. But like so many times before, she rose from the ashes just like a phoenix.

Perhaps one day, she would break this karmic contract. Perhaps one day, she would focus on her well-being. But not today.

That man was exhausting her.

Perhaps one day, she would understand why her soul agreed to the peace treaty that favored him. But for now, it remained a mystery. Until then, she must accept that each soul walked a different path through that human evolution.

If only her soul could reach his, she would whisper,

Oh, tortured soul,
I wish you could find the path of light that dwells within you

Oh, tortured soul,
I wish you could find the path of the inner child that dwells within you

Oh, tortured soul,
I wish you could find the path across the prison walls you've built around you

AMIN

As she retrospectively revisited their story, she was grateful he came into her life. She had to learn the hard way to stand up for herself. She would have preferred a shoulder to lean on.

As she retrospectively revisited their story, she was grateful he came into her life. It helped her to prioritize her well-being first, for the sake of her sanity, and mental and physical health.

As she retrospectively revisited their story, she realized that the experience left deep scars, but she was still able to open her heart. She would even fall in love again … the third time was a charm as they say, or was it more of a scam?

Lynn's Thoughts …

Just about every woman has experienced something similar as to what is written between these lines. So many times, we simply *allow it to happen.* Because of our circumstances, we refuse to say anything, and when we remain quiet, our inner-self awakens and begins to fight back. What makes us who we are will eventually speak up. Our very essence stands on our shoulder nudging us back into reality. Unfortunately, sometimes we blame ourselves instead of the one who is truly to blame.

Anaïssa digs deep into her soul and creates a world of confusion … who do we blame … who do we turn to? We can actually make ourselves ill by refusing to accept what is and moving on.

Why do we do this to ourselves? Why can't we just see the world for what it sometimes is and stop making excuses for ourselves or for others?

We all have an inner light and an inner child. Both will guide us. The inner light illuminates our path. The child holds our hand. However, sometimes our aging-self refuses to listen.

Beautiful Wreckage

Valerie Dawn

The crunching and grinding turned into an echoing thud. A hand grasped the black, metal handle and turned, fingers pushed the cold button that squeaked in protest. The door swung open. An overwhelming odor of fresh dirt filled the emptiness. Darkness loomed even though the sun was shining. Naked in all her glory, she stood strong with beautiful legs that others didn't notice. The hand floated above, caressing and tracing the scars that made her exquisite. What caused each wound? What stories were supported inside the colors that absorbed her so randomly?

She grasped on tightly with both hands and leaned back. Under the forbidden spell, she felt lost, traveling, re-experiencing. A smile touched her lips as the first tear fell.

No going back now.

The aroma of sweetness filled the air – anise and wintergreen mingled together. A hint of what once was, what once existed. Laughter from the shadows merged into undeciphered voices. Sugar clung to her skin and between her lips, the taste of sweetness flowed – love. The experience was hot and hardened as it rolled across her tongue, sticking to her teeth. The fragrance of tangerine changed to coconut and then to black walnut.

Her cheeks warmed, overwhelming cinnamon taking control. Chilly air rushed through an open door. The heat grew as the touch of a silky softness fell between her touch. She massaged the warm log before pinching it. Bits scattered across the table, billowing more sweetness into the air.

It was everywhere now – on her face and the tip of her nose. He had put it there, but she didn't care – she laughed. The sound of a gentle banging grew louder, until it stopped. She relaxed. It was simply time to do it all over again. As they cleaned, they talked, sharing their stories through the velvety richness of the buttery, potato soup. It warmed their bellies as the chilly, fall air swirled.

Red, orange, and brown crinkled and crunched before scattering, falling again before twirling and swirling to a tune only nature could hear. Smaller ones skipped down the hill, laughter engulfing them. It was time to go back. Go back to work for there were more memories to be made. Many more hours, but hardly any time. Yearly, they met and only the place would change. Always close to her birthday. The same sounds and smells, sometimes taking on different positions. It was a continuous tradition, an event that marked the beginning until the end.

That was how life worked. Until it wasn't exciting anymore. When their lives became boring, existing without love or laughter, pain fell within the silence. But that stillness was also the birthplace of regrowth.

For as long as she could remember an internal woman had been there ... been inside her ... somewhat guiding her ... growing, maturing. Never noticed her much, although she often sat beside her, listening to her deepest, darkest secrets and never once telling another. She had shared her hopes and dreams as well as her sorrows. This woman, this strength, held her when she hid her face, catching her tears. Strong and stable when others were weak. Never sure where the woman, the power, had come from, how old she was or when it arrived, she was just always there.

There were others in her life, such as her grandma who was the most important. She had shaped her love, her tradition, and family. Others never fully understood how much spiritual significance grandma had brought into their lives. The essence of love – true ... unconditional.

Spending time with grandma, the young girl began noticing things differently. She accepted why she avoided the one at her childhood home but always looked forward to the one at the house by the water. Maybe it was the memories. Maybe it was the feelings. Maybe it was the expectations. A connection – a spaghetti string that became life – everything touched and aimed straight at her heart.

She now noticed the connections in restaurants, at others' homes, and especially in the classrooms. A singular line that led to her humanity. She absorbed and exchanged dialogue while others remained silent, engaging her, expanding her views, allowing her to be open and honest. Connections she made, during times of excitement or boredom. It was a hard lesson – grief and mourning.

She had the two at her home now. She treated them differently. Not on purpose, more from a point of avoidance or desire – memories and growth. She often started and ended her days with them. The cornerstones of her house. The true witnesses to her happiness turning to rage, before turning to fear. They listened, holding her family's hopes and dreams for her. But it was the anger that made her life burst into flames, one smoking tendril at a time, beginning with laughter and love, and growing into hate.

In reality, it was simply an overarching emptiness.

It hid in the basement, covered in scars. Scratched, carved, and hidden because she never wanted to remember, separating the past and present to avoid the pain. No intention of ever rebuilding that relationship, just moving on. For it was the beginning and the end.

When she replaced it with the one from the other family member, she felt hopeful. It was smaller and carried less baggage. But, they could celebrate as a family again, making new memories. It was the past, however, that echoed, leaking through. Replacement couldn't erase the pain of the present. The one intended on destroying had an army, and she was only one person fighting back.

She lost herself, hating the way she was treated but joined in the crusade to destroy. It listened to the begging, the pleading, and spilled her guts to whomever would listen. But it just stood there while she faded into nothingness. A shadow that no one acknowledged. Instead, she piled her life on top and left it there.

That was how it served until that final day. The day she lost and gained at the same time. No longer could she celebrate with it. Occasionally, during cold and windy nights, she sat with the one hidden in the basement, long enough to fill her needs. But only for a few minutes. Sometimes, it would spend time with her daughter. But generally, it was just there to support a transition.

Maybe I should do something to change that. It deserves more than what we have given it.

The one I had spent the most time with now sat silently in the darkness. Its legs were beautiful and had once enveloped me. It was strong and allowed me to rest in its comfort. I abused it and left my marks that now blemish the once gorgeous complexion. Abusing its curves to the point that one side was glossy and the other marked by fingernail scars. Permanent indentations that never healed. The remnants of our escapades scattered across its face. The smoke dissipated from the passion, and I felt relief. It was my safe place. A place I never wanted to leave. The place where I processed my dreams. It was the first thing I wanted to see in the mornings, and the last thing I wanted to touch before sleep. It was my true connection to the world.

I began measuring my wounds inside the darkness. Climbing the walls I had built to protect myself, I eventually jumped over them. It would help me to be free. I was no longer that scared little girl who believed she needed to be perfect to blend in, to be loved. I became a woman who embraced the darkest of corners. The woman who often failed, carrying that wounded little girl around inside. I just wanted to be loved. Not by many, just by one.

It was called a primal wound – abandonment.

I knew what love was, and I craved it from the one person who would never fulfill my needs. Feeling discarded, insignificant, undesirable, and left behind, my emotions grew and manifested into anxiety. If I were perfect, then I would be good enough. I would then be wanted. But that wish was not achievable. Instead, my desire created an atmosphere for seeds of doubt to grow.

These tiny specks opened, allowing the first strands of darkness to take root, shattering, gnashing into the softest and most vulnerable places. It grew into my spine, slithering around my belly, squeezing and snatching away my life – grasping my dreams and feeding upon my fears.

The vine of doubt fed from my veins, threatening me. I fought back. It stole my vision, changing my sensory input. The first to change was touch, then smell, and finally taste. My body ached. I shied away from others. I avoided eye contact. I felt dirty and unworthy. I was hypervigilant to the presence of others. To brush up against someone or be too close was a torture not worth risking. I needed an escape.

Lovely aromas had turned to a sickening stench, making my stomach churn. When my sense failed so did my appetite. Fatigue set in, and the vine of doubt reached my head, settling in my neck, causing the lymph nodes to grow. They felt like oranges, making it difficult to raise my head, forcing me to worship my shame and guilt. The vine of doubt slithered into my system, rearranging the mechanics of my brain's wiring.

My memories suffocated and faded, taking what was left of my soul. Joy, hope, gratitude, inspiration, awe, amusement, pride, interest, and love evaporated. It was hard to retain information. My motivation shifted from living to simply being, mimicking others' expectations.

The vine slithered into my ears, whispering poisonous words into the deepest canals of my mind. All I could think about was the darkness. A mask was necessary for me to blend in. But the vine was actually a noose around my neck, yanking and tightening, reminding me who was in control.

Perhaps I could end it all?

The vine of doubt multiplied, filling my thoughts with demons that fed on my insecurities.

How could I ever win? Slip an extra pill or maybe ten? Keep walking instead of looking both ways?

The pain would go away. However, when she noticed that my mask had slipped, she told me that she understood and wanted to help, explaining about the invisible war I was fighting. She was the one who made the appointment, not me. I no longer had to carry the wounds and sins of others and be comfortable with the uncomfortable. Forgive myself. No blame, no shame.

I had to find the little girl lost inside me.

But it was the man I had visited weekly that held me together. He caressed my broken pieces. Instead of gluing them, he smashed them into a powdery mixture. The little girl hated him for he was unlocking the doors that held back her demons. A safe place she had hidden.

Thin membranes that clung to my defenses eventually dissolved. I wasn't ready, and it was much easier to simply hate myself than to feel. Self-sabotage was a safe place. An armor that protected the little girl.

Finally, I stood face-to-face with her. Never actually meeting her before, I listened. I never mourned her in front of him. I cried in private, only apologizing for building the walls in the first place. It was time to tear them down. I had to free her.

Once a week, I visited. Six days would pass before we would talk again. We navigated the paths using a broken compass. It was often difficult to find true north. The only way forward was to step back. Back to the place where it had started. The place where no vine of doubt had yet taken root.

Digging in deep, I had to see what the little girl could not see. I had to finish the never-ending story she could not read. I had to find someone who shared that awful day with her. Someone who refused to believe her. Someone one who could have changed everything but turned and covered her eyes. It was the day the vine was planted.

The conversation opened a dialogue with disgust and rage.

It was a chapter closed that needed to be opened. I wanted to free the little girl. But would my actions actually free her? Or would the vine of doubt grow? It was a betrayal – me making excuses, protecting the perpetrator. The one that brought a lifetime of pain to the innocent.

The vine hunted the little girl as I confronted the someone and asked for forgiveness. He did not say anything. An eclipse of darkness lingered, allowing the vine of doubt to regrow. Numbness swelled, overwhelming my feelings, rushing into my soul. The mask would fit snugly and hide the enlarging emptiness that would soon consume me. Accepting the memories would mean accepting the pain, giving the little girl stronger material to rebuild the walls. We could then live without our dreams and nightmares. We could function without our hopes. I smiled.

But what was happiness?

The truth made us question our past. The truth would also tear down the walls that had stunted our growth. If I accepted the someone back, would the truth be revealed?

My life had been a lie.

The seed of doubt had been intentionally planted. I had been told I wasn't lovable, that I was never wanted. He had given the vine a solid place to be grown and that place was inside me. The demons were handed to me because of my lack of strength.

The vine, however, was now old. It had haunted me for many years. A generational doubt, planted by my mother and passed on to her daughter. A behavior to be condoned before allowing anyone to be happy. Once planted, the seed could be re-seeded in my offspring – devouring the good, regaining power with each female born. Once the vine was transferred, the demons would take hold of the new host. A game of cat and mouse, manufacturing fear producing more demons.

The little girl knew the things the vine was doing were wrong. Together, they had a new strength, their memories. They once ran when their life was threatened. A repetitive chapter in their story. But no more.

They had obeyed, learning to be faster than the someone making holes in the door. Fighting back would only bring a new punishment, a harsher punishment. They wore an eyepatch when they couldn't move fast enough. They cried when that someone had cut off their ear. They should have just ran faster. The seed was planted because they were a little girl instead of a little boy. Although he was no longer a part of their lives, his demons remained. And now, they would have to battle the demons together.

Every day she grew stronger. The visits with that little girl became productive. Sometimes they'd cry and sometimes they'd laugh. But together, they'd explore and grow and dream. They rested and battled, but always together. The little girl never grew up, but she inspired to be fearless.

A hand wiped away the tears as they stared at those beautiful scars on the table in the basement. The hand caressed the frame, rubbing the tears into the grain of wood.

It was grandma's kitchen table.

Those flaws made it more beautiful as she said her final goodbyes to the little girl.

Lynn's Thoughts …

I cannot count the number of times that I have used something from my past to steady my future. Valerie excellently captures how a past trauma can and will affect us forever. At what point, at what level, does forgiveness surrender to acceptance? That is something we may never know, but something our author tackles.

As we grow, we must come to accept that those who shaped our lives were once young too. They once had a life and they too had to learn how to accept their past. Unfortunately, so many are not willing to break the chains. Instead, they pass the hurt along for the next generation to bear instead of standing firm and fighting back.

Valerie's unnamed character lived her life through her grandmother's table. A love affair without a beginning or ending … deep emotions with no depth … scars without a wound. All held together by an inner child that was loved, hated, honored, and resented. An inner child that was harbored within the world of the adults.

So many children are abandoned by their parents. Left to wander the world alone. Then again, many children are abandoned with their parents still in the house. I'm not sure which is worse. Both hold an emotional abuse that is ever-lasting.

Valerie's use of a vine to describe the emotions that bind her character was most clever. A seed planted by the father and nurtured by the mother's inability to accept a dark truth. If not for the grandmother's table, strong wood with an everlasting aroma of memories, perhaps this unnamed character would never have found her true voice.

Birds

Elizabeth Elder

"Hold on, I want to close this window. The birds are driving me crazy with their incessant chatter. It's five in the morning, and I can hardly hear myself think. There … at least the rain has cleared. Why are you calling me? It's five a.m."

"I could see that your light's on. From my kitchen window, you know … the one above the porch."

"Oh, oh, now I see, your light's on too. Yes, I'm in my kitchen. I think I've been up for hours. I cannot stop thinking. I'm counting everything that's gone. Do you ever do that? The list keeps growing. I am the lone survivor of a past that is so lost it could only be found in pieces … in the faded pages of some old storybook, some discarded tome about that girl I used to be, and the characters around her. Oh, my. My life is a soggy, old thing trampled in the rain. It's nothing but phrases in puddles. Even my memories are like swimming through fog. There's my brother, Tom, standing there with suds all over his car, and our old dog, Hudson, flopped in the flower bed.

The images slide into tatters. There's my first date, and the skating I loved. Roommates and college friends … probably most are dead now, and I cannot remember their names. Not only that … hold on, I'm going to make some coffee. I'm not prepared …"

"I have coffee, if …"

"No, I have coffee. I mean, I'm not prepared for what's coming … this loss after loss after loss. People I loved. Places I never got to. Books I never read. Or wrote. And it's not only personal. I think if the world were at least a little familiar, we could bear the personal losses … the way our parents and their parents did, back when the home, instead of the Internet, was where life began and ended … where we learned the little cultural things, like writing thank you notes, folding towels so the edges don't show, ironing a shirt, sitting up straight in a chair. Oh, my. Whatever I can teach my children and grandchildren today does not apply to anything. Even grammar is superfluous. You know, it's no wonder we have these childish polarities of opinions in our country. There is no grammatical mechanism left for structuring complex ideas into intelligible explanations. We've lost the form for thinking. Remember the subordinate clause, and how it could articulate a nuance of an independent thought? Texting did it in. And when did *text* become a verb anyway? Oh, my. I don't disagree that technology systems can be useful … providing there are young people around who are patient enough to explain them. But such time it all takes. You and I are of the generation of people who had to learn both ways. First, we were students of our parents, and now we are students of our children. I miss that chronological allegiance. Do you know what I mean? That's a big loss on my list. You know?"

"Hmmm … ah … it's not my primary interest, so to speak."

"And I miss watching respectable news. Remember civility? Honest pride and earned advancement, acceptance without sarcasm, the honor of truth? Gentility? Wait a minute. Where is that box of cereal … oh, here it is, right where I put it. But, I think the biggest one on my list comes from this sobering recognition of the fragility of everything natural. We need to be concerned about our Earth now, instead of being comforted by its constancy. Oh, how innocent we were … how unsophisticated and mindless. I don't think I told you about my family's cottage. Did I? I know I haven't known you long, and we haven't talked much. Did I mention it?"

"I don't think so."

"Our family spent summers in a beach house years ago … over on the western shore. Cabins dotted the fields along the rural road that meandered up the hill. We sailed and swam and dug clams. We ran up to the tracks when the train came, so we could wave to the conductors. A watermelon would be cooling in the natural spring at the edge of the yard while we played kick-the-can after supper. Oh, those summer nights. My cousins still own the cottage, but they could not hold on to its aura. It sits like a little mushroom among towering year-round homes crowded together one after the other, up the hill and along the shore. The train tracks are now a bike path, and the bikers chuckle at the frumpy, old cabin hunkered amongst its overpowering neighbors. Its past is in the air, I guess, and in the spirit of those few of us who lived it. Is that all we have … the spirit of the past … to push us on? Well, it's good to talk about it. It really is. I feel better, thanks to you. Do you have plans for the day? The sun's beginning to streak through those trees, just since we've been talking."

"No, but I heard the birds. They woke me up. I remembered what my son told me about why they make such a fuss in the morning."

"Your son, Matthew?"

"Yes, Matthew. He said birds live in communities. They all know who's around … other birds, I mean. The first thing they want to do in the morning is to announce themselves and check in with each other. The earliest bird, all puffed up and confident, starts with, 'I am over here, this is my place.' And all the other birds, one by one, or at the same time, chatter out their own kind of clarity, announcing, 'Here I am up in this tree over here.' 'And I am over here.' 'All's well. I hear you. I'm awake, too.' 'This is where I am.' So that's what the ruckus is about. Matthew said it's the spirit of the moment that matters. That's what makes the birdsong."

"The spirit of the moment. Oh, my. Hold on, I'm cutting up this banana. Is that why you called … to tell me about the birds and what Matthew said?"

"No. I only thought of what he said because the birds woke me up. I called because I saw your light from my kitchen window."

Lynn's Thoughts …

An older mind fumbling through private thoughts in the pre-dawn hours … perhaps two?

Time is a funny thing, counting the number of times we circle our sun, or the number of rotations before beginning anew. Morning, night, morning, night, an ever evolving existence. Animals simply eat and sleep, but a human adds another variable … thought. We must analyze our minutes, our days, our weeks, or our years. Does it really matter how many times we revolve around the sun?

Do birds talk to each other? Do they compare their children's accomplishments … their failures … their challenges? Or do they simply exist? Should we simply exist?

Elizabeth looks at life through the eyes and ears of two women who are comparing the morning rays with birds. How does life fit into this equation? Does it even matter?

What I found intriguing with this piece is how insignificant life is and how much emphasis we add to it simply by including *thought.* Otherwise, we too would simply soar through the world on a fresh current never once turning to look back.

BRIDGE

D. M. Clemens

Layers of frozen rain had already cased on the trees outside One Horse Bar, and the storm wasn't over yet. Branches grew steadily heavier and occasionally, one would crack and fall in a blast of frosty shrapnel. Electricity was tenuous and anyone who drove to the watering hole was taunting fate.

"Bart's an old man's name." Bridgette Cain claimed a stool next to a man she'd seen around town but never met. Her thick, black eyeshadow dominated her eyes, her t-shirt too tight.

In the dim room, neon colors dyed the air and pooled on varnished tables. The diamondback rattles and coyote skulls mounted on walls were older than most clients, and a pair of ketchup and vinegar bottles looked even older.

"Since you're not old ..." – she smirked – "... it must be a family name."

Father Bartholomew Claghorn glanced at Bridge's face for only a second. His wind-burnt nose held up his wire spectacles, and his neck girded an aging cashmere scarf. "It was my father's name."

"Father Bartholomew's father was called Bartholomew," Bridge mused. "It's a tongue twister."

The priest considered a different stool but decided it wouldn't help. There were only two other patrons at One Horse tonight, Dickie Crane, a retired electrician, and Abe Stansen, a car salesman, whose second job was whiskey. Blending into a crowd was out of the question.

Father Bart was called to Natagwa twelve years ago when a stroke snatched his predecessor mid-dream. The freshly collared clergyman had arrived with a trunk of books, an east coast education, and a desire to serve. Now, the dwindling parish he had inherited and the promiscuous tabby that came with it were both on their last legs.

Sarge, the ex-marine owner of One Horse, cracked a beer for Bridge without being asked.

Father Bart opened an antique silver holder.

"Can't smoke in here," Sarge scowled.

"C'mon, Sarge," Bridge replied. "Wires are broken, trees are fallin', and we're all gonna die on the drive home. Feels like the end of the fuckin' world."

Sarge snapped a towel from under the bar and walked away.

Bart swiped a match, touching the flame to Bridge's smoke before his own. At the far end of the counter, Dickie squinted at the lawbreakers, fishing a foil pack from his flannel shirt as Abe extracted a pack from his khakis. Tobacco clouds blurred One Horse's neon signs for the first time in twenty-some years, and it did feel like the end of something.

"How about," Bridge stated, "since it's the end of the world, I'll be your priest tonight. You confess your sins, and I'll forgive them."

"That's a good offer." Bart kept his eyes on the foam riding the brown sea of beer in his glass. "And you are?"

"Bridge … short for Bridgette," she replied.

Bart wouldn't have a lit cigarette between his fingers if it wasn't for the girl on the stool next to him, so he played along. "Forgive me, Bridge, for I have sinned. This is my second pack today."

Bridge laughed. "I sentence you to four beers and three whiskeys … drink and be forgiven." She finished off her green bottle.

Bart drank the rest of the brown sea and set his glass down. "One time, I quit for a week. Then at the end of a bad day, I saw old butts in the dustbin." His reflection stared back from behind the bar. "They were covered in vacuum dirt, and I smoked them anyway."

"That's pretty desperate." Bridge motioned Sarge for another round.

"Want to know the lesson?" Bart asked.

Bridge hesitated. "Take out the trash?"

"No." He crushed the dying cigarette in a coffee mug Sarge had given him to use an ashtray. "When you walk away from something, don't keep any trace of it."

"You should use that in a sermon."

"I would lose the seven people who still come on Sundays."

Two beers down. Sarge watched them with his Semper Fidelis arm bent on the counter.

"How'd you end up here?" Bridge asked.

"In Natagwa?" Bart craved another cigarette.

"At One Horse," Bridge added. "I've never seen you here."

The priest clinked a fresh beer against hers. "It's the only place open in a storm like this."

"Too low rent for you." She shook her head. "Somethin' bad happened today?"

Bart drank instead of answering.

"Tell me," she said. "Tell Father Bridgette what happened."

Three beers down, and the wind rattled the door like it was looking for a way inside.

"My parents've been married for forty-three years," he said. "They live in Virginia."

"And now they're getting a divorce?" she asked.

"Now they're getting a divorce," he repeated.

She looked at Bart for a minute. "I had period cramps, so my day was worse."

Bart pinched off his spectacles and considered the challenge. "I burnt my eggs and went hungry."

"Yeah?" She laughed. "My horse broke his leg, and I had to shoot 'im."

"I was abducted by the FBI." Bart chuckled.

"I was actually abducted by aliens."

Bart replaced his glasses and thought for a minute. "I was lonely." Four beers down, and he studied his warped self in the mirror. "Sarge, can we get a couple of whiskeys over here?" Bart yelled.

The barman gripped a red, labeled bottle by its neck just as the front door crashed open. A pharmacist called Juan Padilla wrestled through the frame in his dripping parka. "You all hiding from the storm in here?"

Abe looked up from his seat and snickered. "You hiding from your wife?"

Juan laughed.

One whiskey down, and a slide guitar in the speakers overhead modulated up a key.

"Do you believe in angels?" Bridge asked the priest. "Or demons?"

"Of a sort."

"That's vague." She held up her shot glass and twisted it with her fingers. "Really, fuckin' vague. You pastors love holdin' back."

Bart felt surprised, and his eyes met hers for the first time.

"You're in charge of a door that people wanna go through," she said. "You're a fuckin' bouncer for God is what you are. The more people think you know secret shit they don't know, the more powerful you are." Her gaze never left Bart's. "And the crazy thing is that people want you to know that secret shit." Bridge leaned closer. "Because if *you* know answers, then there *are* answers."

Two whiskeys down, and Sarge washed and stacked glasses while keeping an eye on Bridge, like he always did.

"You have a history with the church?" Bart asked.

"You could say that. When I was in high school, the church elders cast demons outta me ... rebellion and independence." She grinned. "Also, lasciviousness. You know what that is?"

"I'm a priest," he answered.

Sarge refilled Dickie's shot glass just as the neon faltered for a second. All the souls in One Horse waited to see if the electricity would hold. Sarge dug out candles and the drinking resumed. "'Bout to get romantic in here," he warned.

"Have you ever done an exorcism?" Bridge asked.

"I've yet to meet someone possessed." Bart tossed his matchbook to the barman.

"Natagwa is crawlin' with possessed people," Bridge stated. "Accordin' to my church elders, this town is a spiritual battleground."

Bart frowned. "Your church says that?"

"It's what all the churches say around here." Bridge squinted and shrugged. "You don't know what other churches think?"

"Catholics aren't part of the team in Natagwa." Bart offered her a smoke. "Why do they think people are possessed?"

"Because of the lumines and the demonic activity they left behind."

"You mean illuminati? I thought they were an off-brand of the freemasons."

"They are … and thugs and warlocks." Bridge laughed. "Christians ran them out of town, but apparently the demons stayed."

"What makes the churches believe that?"

"Haunted trees." Smoke escaped between her words. "Stories about an old woman who lives in the ground and comes out at night. And people acting weird."

"A woman who lives in the ground?"

Bridge nodded. "There's always been a weird hole in the middle of Seller's field. When we were kids, we used to throw trash in it. Lumines said the Auspex lives down there. She comes out at night and sits on a flat rock by the woods."

Bart smiled like a scientist who could see through the magic tricks. "What does the Auspex want?"

"She marks people." Bridge nodded. "If it's you, she comes into your room at night, and then you wake up the next day with your hair cut off, sprinkled in a circle around the bed."

"And then what?" Bart asked.

"I don't know. I don't think it's happened in a long time."

"Of course," he replied. "Did your church believe in the Auspex?"

"No." She shook her head. "They just thought that the Lumines set off a beehive of demons with their witchcraft. But my ass hasn't seen a pew for a long time. So, who knows?"

The wind outside spontaneously howled. The door opened and bitter rain pelted the linoleum. Dickie, who had one fist almost through a coat sleeve, headed into the storm. Juan and Abe exited behind him.

"Final round," Sarge announced. A jet of red whiskey hit each tumbler. "Bridge, you making friends with a priest? This ain't gonna end well."

Bridge's eyes narrowed.

Bart laughed. "In a town this size, you don't have to meet each other to know each other. Especially, if you're a little different."

"It ain't gonna end well," Sarge repeated, aiming a dirty rag at a bucket near the sink.

Bridge slapped her hand on the counter. "What do you mean *different*? You're white and heterosexual and a Christian. If you ask me, you're pretty much like everyone else in Natagwa."

"You don't have any idea what kind of a sexual man I am," Bart replied.

"I have some idea."

"I'm the only priest in a Protestant town. I'm not exactly invited for Sunday dinners."

She stared at her reflection. "How am I different?"

"You're in a bar, in the middle of a storm." Bart replied. "The rest of Natagwa is sleeping."

"I thought maybe because I'm a slut." Bridge pushed away the offer for a last whiskey.

Normally, Bart would say no one deserves that label, but tonight was different. "Why do you take people home?"

Bridge didn't answer.

Maybe it was because no one had ever asked her before. Maybe it was because he was a priest, or maybe it was because of the storm. But, he had obviously hit a soft spot.

"I don't know … maybe being addicted to something is like havin' a toddler trapped in your head. Any time it takes over, you're fucked." She stared into the old mirror. "Every night, I'm standin' on a bridge, and I never know if I'm gonna get down or jump off." Her brow wrinkled. "And in the mornin' … I couldn't tell you why

I was on that fuckin' bridge in the first place." As if to make the point, she jumped off the chair. "I gotta visit the ladies' room."

The black night flooded the bar, and the neon signs died like they were candles snuffed out by the wind.

"Here we go," Sarge said.

Bridge's fingers found Bart's arm. "Come home with me," she whispered. "It doesn't have to be …"

A match head hissed to life.

"It can be whatever," she said.

Bart's answer was a hand on the small of her back, guiding her toward the register. The money drawer clicked and the bartender slapped coins on the counter.

"Don't do it, priest," Sarge whispered. "You'll end up explaining to the doc why you got green foam coming outta your prick. A priest with the clap'll spread like wildfire. You can say adios to your seven Catholics."

Bridge saluted Sarge with her middle finger.

Sarge saluted back. "Drive safe, you two."

Bart zipped up the toddler's raincoat. On Halloween, he had read ghost stories to a grade schoolers. He could have hung a Christmas star and enjoyed the day with a middle schooler. Or maybe eat over-cooked eggs with his wife inside their empty nest. It was another life that had passed within the middle of a freezing rainstorm.

Bridge's left arm hugged his waist, nudging at his soul. It was what could have been.

He was thankful to be the front spoon because his body was rigid with biological drive. Bart didn't ask and she didn't offer. But it was a beautiful twist, ending the day under a blanket with another. Warmth saturating his cells, seeping into his inner spirit.

He thought about how many men had slept on these sheets, and he couldn't say why cigarettes were a better addiction than warm skin. Throwing the first stones and all that.

Just before dawn, a sterile moonbeam traced along the fault line in the clouds, painting a silhouette on Bridge's frozen window. It was the shadow of a bent woman with graying braids, dragging fresh cut hair behind her.

Lynn's Thoughts ...

Two souls from extreme ends of the universe collide on a dark and stormy night. One Horse Bar becomes the gravity that holds the two together. One who's life exists within the shadows, and the other wishing they could hide in the shadows. Neither living their expectations of what they believed should have been.

The ending for me was an interesting turn of affairs. I may read it differently than others, but isn't that what reading is all about? To pull from the lines the message that touches our heart? I concluded that our father is not quiet happy being the type of *father* he ended up being. And ... if he had taken a different path, perhaps he could have become a real father with a real family and perhaps real children. And the girl, what did she want out of life other than to feel loved and protected?

D.M. Clemens tackles an interesting blight within our current lives. Have we lived what we were supposed to live? Are we who we are supposed to be? Or did we simply allow fate to mold our existence? A heavy concept to contemplate. Who are we? Where are we?

And the heaviest question of all ... are we happy?

Eden's Rain

Samuel G. Tooma

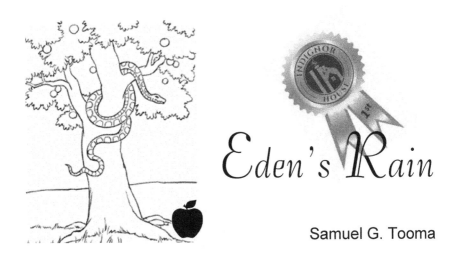

"Deborah ... your father and I do not support you camping by yourself in the Canadian wilderness. It's too dangerous for a young girl to be alone like that."

"Mom, I'm not a *girl*. I'm twenty-five, an *adult*, and can make my own decisions."

"True, but why would you even consider such a thing?"

"You know why, Mom. I just ended my engagement with Richard, and I'm depressed. Plus, it seems like the world is going down the toilet. You follow the news. Countries invading their neighbors, shootings in schools, church attendance dropping, abortions and divorces at an all time high, oceans dying, sexual immorality's now the norm, and we're in the middle of a nasty presidential election. I could go on and on. I need to get away and forget this crap."

"How will you survive in the wilderness for two weeks?"

"I've backpacked since I was seventeen. I can take care of myself. *Trust me*."

"This is insane. But alright, when do you need to be at the airport?"

"I'm meeting Fred Gibbons at eight tomorrow morning."

"We'll take you, but I agree with your mother. I don't like this. Do you trust this *Fred Gibbons*?"

"Yes, Dad. He's an experienced bush pilot, and he knows what he's doing. He's familiar with the wilds of British Columbia, and I've known him for years."

"Deborah, we love you so much. I hope you understand our concern."

"I do, Mom, and I love both of you more than you know."

"There's Lake Bare." Fred pointed out the port window. "We're landing at Lake Eden ... half mile east. See it?"

"It's small. Can you land on it?"

"Done it many times. Hold on." Fred banked and began his descent. The plane barely cleared the cypress trees at the edge of the lake, but the pontoon touched the water seconds later.

With the plane secured at the pier, Fred smiled. "Come on, Deb. Let's get your gear to the camp site."

"Okay Deb, you're on your own. You sure you'll be okay?"

"I'm fine. Already looking forward to being alone."

"I'll be back in two weeks. Remember, cell service sucks here. Got that?"

"Yup."

"I'm serious. You probably won't see another human for two weeks. Last chance to change your mind."

"See you in two, Fred. Have a safe trip back to Seattle and to that cesspool we call the world."

A short time later, I waved as he flew over the camp.

For six days, I thoroughly enjoyed my desired solitude. I caught fish and picked blueberries. My backpacking experience was proving invaluable. However, on the morning of the seventh, I was about to start my day when a loud explosion rocked the ground. I crawled out of the tent, shaking, to see what happened. A streak of light zoomed over my head. A blazing fireball ripped through the trees and was now sizzling in the center of the lake. Water bubbled as steam filled the sky.

Need to get to the pier ... get a closer look.

More explosions. I glanced up, and the sky was laced with blazing streaks plummeting to the ground.

Meteors? What's going on?

More fireballs hit and flames lashed out setting fire to the dense brush. Standing motionless between the trees and lake, I ducked as another fireball fell from the cloudless sky. A large flame flared only a few yards in front of me. I darted behind the closest tree and hid from the flying debris. Embers rained down, stinging my face and arms. My tent burned. I screamed and grabbed a pail of water I had been using. The fire died and steam hissed. Embers floated around me, covering everything as if fiery snowflakes were falling. More tremors and flaming orbs again shattered the ground. The lake crackled and bubbled as if lit by an unseen fire as another meteor hit the far side of the lake. A deafening explosion echoed, and I covered my ears and screamed.

I grabbed my empty backpack and shoved in dried food, water-purification pills, a butane lighter, and any other items I would need. With my rifle clinging to my shoulder, I needed to head for the larger

Lake Bare. The fire was spreading and fast. The smoke thickened, making it difficult to breathe. I coughed and my eyes stung, tears blinded me. A pair of my clean underpants worked as a make-shift face mask. It helped me breathe through the smoke, but the heat was overbearing. More explosions, and I glanced back as a flaming bough fell, hit my tent, and engulfed it in flames.

I had to get to Lake Bare, but I knew getting there would not be easy nor safe. Flames were dancing across the treetops, giving the landscape an eerie manifestation of hell. My half-mile journey to Lake Bare turned into a three-hour nightmare. My face felt scorched. Twice, falling debris severely burned my arms. Only adrenalin kept me from panicking. I pushed on.

I dodged fire after fire. When Lake Bare filled my view, so did the fireballs. The smoke grew thicker and denser. My eyes burned. The temperature was swelting, and the wild and hot wind sent chills down my spine.

A large clearing near Lake Bare provided some safety from the expanding fires, but the fireballs were still falling. I stood in the middle of the clearing and prayed. After what seemed like an eternity, the fireballs trickled to only a few. I dropped my gear, stripped bare, and ran to the lake's cooler water. Rinsing off the sweat and soot felt comforting, almost natural. Dead fish floated around me, their eyes wide, staring into the heavens. My heart pounded, and I sighed.

Back at the clearing, I treated my burns with my first aid kit. One of the fish I gathered would make the perfect meal. I collected several glowing embers and soon had it cooked. The heat was oppressive, and I thought it ironic that the fires were blazing all around and threatening my life. Yet I still needed one to cook my catch.

The large clearing seemed odd in the middle of the Canadian wilderness. But I felt safe there. The trees were still burning, surrounding me with a dancing wall of reds and yellows. It was then

I noticed a dirt road. Perhaps this was a place for visitors to park and enjoy the lake. I was safe in the clearing for now, but I knew that if I stayed here, I would die.

The wooded area was just too dangerous to cross, but perhaps the dirt road could be a way out. The lake was somewhat protecting me, but I couldn't remain here much longer. Fred would never find me through the dense smoke. The road would have to lead me somewhere - *somewhere with people*? Looking at the now impassable road, I had to accept that I was trapped. The fire was just too hot.

For the next three days, I remained inside the clearing with several deer and other small critters. They looked scared and confused. We would eye each other, but never once did we cross into each other's safety. My eyes burned and watered. It was painful to breathe. My precious drinking water was measured and calculated. The lake my only relief to the blisters growing on my arms and face. The meteor strikes had finally stopped. But the fires refused to die.

Would Fred ever find me?

Several more days passed, and the fires continued to burn. I felt weak. I knew I would probably die here, inside this meadow, along with these poor wild animals.

I prayed and whispered aloud to my parents. "I'm sorry, Mom, Dad. You were right. I should have listened. I pray this horrible thing is not happening to you." I sipped the last of my precious water, and began to cry, knowing that my end was near. Then, something hit my face. A drop. A clear, slender drop. Then another and another.

"Rain!" I screamed. "Thank you, Lord, for hearing my prayer. There is still hope for me and these innocent animals."

The frightened deer stared at me, curiously tilting their heads.

At the lake, I gathered several dead fish and cooked them before the rain snuffed out my fire. By nightfall, I was soaked, and my campfire was just a memory. The temperature had dropped, and I shivered, feeling cold and vulnerable.

At dawn's first light, the rain had quenched the wildfires, but the sky remained dark with heavy clouds and smoke. With my water bottles now full of fresh rainwater, I hefted my backpack and shouldered my rifle. Using one of my shirts, I tied my cooked fish to my belt. Slowly, I trudged down the dirt road allowing the rain to soothe my burnt skin.

For two long days, I slogged through the rain and mud. Traveling was slow because of the downed trees, standing water, thick, slippery mud, and low visibility. Twice I slipped, twisting my ankle, slowing me down even more. My already painful burns were now open, mud-caked sores. The air felt cold on my wet skin. I shivered but pushed on. The rain continued, and the odor of burnt, wet wood felt overpowering. I was exhausted. The dirt road ahead seemed to be an endless brown, muddy alley of doom.

On the third day, the rain finally stopped, and the sun poked out from behind the clouds. I dried my clothes under the welcomed sun. With minimal sleep behind me, I rested on a flat rock and fell into a deep sleep. When I awoke, I felt somewhat rejuvenated. With renewed hope and determination, I continued my trek down the long, endless road with only two fish and three bags of trail mix remaining.

Can't waste my food.

The ground was slippery. I was very weak. If I fell, I probably would not be able to get back up. My twisted ankle pounded, and my burns stung mercilessly. Ignoring the pain, I kept walking. The road seemed to wander through the destruction with no signs of ending. I wearily sat on a rock and took a deep breath.

Will I die here - alone?

I was weak and struggling to remain upright. It was dusk, I knew the sun would soon fall beyond the distant ridge. Reluctantly,

I accepted that I could go no farther. I probably would not survive the night. I fell to my knees unable to move. I dejectedly looked at the mud and cried. Through my tears, I noticed them - *footprints* - coming from the opposite direction leading into the charred forest.

Holy crap! Those prints were made after the rain stopped. Otherwise, they'd have been washed away. *Someone's alive! I'm not alone.*

With a sudden burst of adrenalin, I pushed myself upright and followed the prints. At several spots, the mud was greatly disturbed.

Must be hurt. Falling. "Hello! Hello? Can anybody hear me?" I picked up my pace.

The tracks were leading to an opening in the rocks. I followed them to a cave's entrance.

"Hello? Anybody here?" I cautiously entered, my rifle at the ready. "Anybody here?"

A weak male voice replied, "Yes. Help!"

Several yards in, a man was lying on his back.

"Are you okay?" I stepped closer. "Are you hurt?"

"Injured. Hungry. Very weak."

I knelt by his side. "I'm Deborah. I can help. Where are you hurt?"

He smiled. "Hi, Deborah." He pointed to his left side.

"Thirsty?"

He nodded.

I handed him a water bottle. "Drink slowly."

I carefully opened his shirt. A large bruise on his side was caked with dried blood. I took another bottle and gently poured water over the wound. He grimaced.

"Sorry," I whispered. "But I've got to clean this out. I need to see what's going on."

He nodded and winced again.

"What's your name?"

"Dave."

"Nice to meet you, Dave."

"Deborah, you're an angel from heaven."

I giggled. "Well, Dave, I've been called many things but never an angel." I continued to inspect his wound. "You have one hell of a bruise and a deep laceration. But in my not-so-expert opinion, you probably have a broken rib or two. Can't tell without an X-ray."

"Got an X-ray machine farther back in the cave."

I laughed.

Dave took a deep breath and winced. "Hurts when I breathe. Can't move."

"Hungry? I've have some fish we can share. Don't have much. Gotta go easy on the water too."

"'We?" he repeated. "You said, we? Thank you. Thought I was going to die in here by myself."

"You are going to die, Dave. Just not today. I'll take care of you. It's getting dark. There's more light near the cave's entrance. If I help, can you make it there?"

"I'll try."

With my support, Dave and I struggled to move closer to the light. I looked again at his injuries.

"I'll wrap your ribs. Try not to breathe while I do."

"You're funny, Deborah."

"Call me, Deb. All my friends do."

Dave nodded." It's an honor to be your friend, Deb."

As I pulled gauze from my first aid kit, I asked, "Tell me, how'd you survive the firestorm and end up here?"

Dave coughed. "Working on my PhD in Biology … British Columbia University." He shuddered. "Studying why the Great Horned Owl population is decreasing in the northwest. Come here often to gather data for my thesis. That's how I found this cave. On my way here, the meteors –" He flinched. "One hit close … knocked my truck off the road. Only could save some junk food and my broadband radio."

"Where's your radio?"

"Back in the cave with the X-ray machine." He smiled weakly. "Batteries dead. Useless. What's your story?"

I chuckled at the thought of an X-ray machine inside a cave. "I was here a week before the meteors hit. No radio or cell service. What happened?"

"NASA crashed another rocket on a large asteroid that was going to miss us by millions of miles. Trying to see if they could divert one that big. In case the Earth was at risk from an asteroid strike in the future."

"I'm aware of NASA's program. What happened next?"

"Something went wrong. Didn't deflect it. Pushed it toward us. It grazed off the moon and exploded into millions of pieces. This happened the day before I drove here from Vancouver. Didn't know how bad things were until it started raining asteroid fireballs."

I shook my head.

"Barely made it to this cave. My truck's a mile down the road in a ditch. I kept listening on the broadband. Wanted to know how bad everything was."

"And?"

"It's bad. Meteors blanketed the world. Fires and poisonous gases everywhere. Most, if not all the big cities … destroyed. Untold millions … dead. Even worse, large meteors fell into the oceans, and tsunamis are predicted to flood coastal areas. Earthquakes and volcanoes worldwide. When my batteries died, the last report was that all life on Earth was in jeopardy."

"Unbelievable. How'd you get hurt?"

"When the rain stopped, I wanted to find my truck. See what I could salvage. Didn't get far. Fell in the mud. Hit a rock. No food. No water. Can barely walk. Knew I was a dead man … until you found me."

I smiled. "We can't stay here. No food or fresh water left. If you can stand the pain, we'll try to make it to your truck tomorrow."

"Not sure I can, but I'll try."

"I've got pain killers in my first-aid kit. That should help."

Dave sighed. "Before my batteries died, all I heard on the radio was static. I couldn't raise anyone. It's like no one's alive out there."

"We'll need new batteries. Any in your truck?"

"Yes. Unless my truck's destroyed."

"Okay. I'm going to immobilize your chest now as best I can. Get ready for some serious pain."

The next morning, we began our arduous and slow journey down the muddy road. When we reached Dave's truck, it was of no use. A large flaming tree had fallen across it. We did find batteries that had miraculously survived. They proved useless, all we heard was static.

"Seems bad. Even the emergency broadcasting stations aren't transmitting."

I shook my head.

"Listen, four of my friends were about an hour behind me on the drive from Vancouver. They were going to help me gather data before swimming in Lake Bare."

"I know where Lake Bare is. It saved my life. Let's see if we can find your friends. Where does this road lead?"

"We're in Bonaparte Provincial Park. This road eventually connects to Route 5."

"How far to Route 5?"

"About fifteen miles."

"With your chest wound and my twisted ankle, it's going to be a very slow walk. No way will we make it today."

That afternoon, we found what was left of Dave's friends' van. It had been struck by a meteor and was barely recognizable as a vehicle. Dave fell to his knees and bowed his head. Four charred bodies were still buckled to their seats. I hugged him.

"They were my best friends," he whispered, "and their girlfriends."

"I'm so sorry. Let's pray for them and their families?"

"Please," he replied, wiping his tears with the back of his hand. "I'd be honored and so would they."

After our prayers, Dave remained on his knees and cried. I held him, and we wept together.

"There's nothing we can do for them now," he finally stated. "We should move on."

He stood with my help, sighed, and we continued our painful journey to Route 5. As we walked, areas of green forest appeared.

"Looks like the fireballs from hell didn't hit here. It's eerie," I said. "Green on the right side of the road and black char on the left."

"There is hope, Deb." He took a painful deep breath. "I'm worn out, and this pain is killing me. Can we stop for the night?"

"I'm tired and hurting too. Let's look at the bright side … we have green trees to sleep under."

He smiled and nodded.

We settled in at our makeshift campsite, and Dave started a fire with my butane lighter. I searched the forest for anything edible.

"Dave! I found berries and roots. There's a spring of fresh water not far. I even found a wild apple tree."

We ate in silence as Dave fought back his tears. The sky darkened into night, and he smiled at me. "Thank you. You saved my life."

A warm feeling soared through my heart. I reached out and took his hands in mine. When our hands touched, our eyes widened.

"Did you feel that, Deb?"

"Yes. It's like electricity running up my arms, and a strong sense of … *warmth.*"

"Me too. A feeling of peace and a need to protect you. Wow!"

We continued to hold hands and look at each other. The strong feelings increased. He pulled me to him, and we embraced. Gently at first, and then stronger. We didn't speak and fell asleep in each other's arms.

In the morning, we awoke with severe stomach cramps and feeling horribly sick.

"Those apples," I said. "Something inside me warned me not to eat them. I should have listened."

"What happened between us last night?"

"I don't know. But from the first moment I saw you in that cave, I've felt a connection. A strong connection."

"Same here. And when our hands touched, all I wanted to do was hold you."

"I can't explain it," I replied. "Very strange."

"There's something else. When we walked into the treed forest yesterday, my side started feeling better. I can now breathe without pain."

"Me too. My ankle doesn't hurt. And look at my face and arms. The burns are almost healed. Let me see your side."

He opened his shirt.

"Dave, your bruises are gone, and your laceration is almost healed. How can this be? It's a miracle." I thought for a moment and added, "There's another miracle too."

"What?"

"The rain. If it hadn't rained when it did, we'd both be dead and never have met. That rain brought us together."

We embraced before beginning our journey again. As we walked, our hands remained tightly entwined.

"Last night," Dave stated, "I heard insects, coyotes, wolves, and other animals."

"Yes, and look, birds are everywhere."

"There's animal life all around us. It seems like we're in a perfect place in the middle of utter desolation."

"But why can't we hear anyone on the radio?" I asked.

"Don't know."

As we walked, we talked.

"Tell me a little more about yourself," I said. "Are you Canadian?"

"Born here. Twenty-five and single."

A feeling of relief swept over me. "Serious girlfriend?"

"Nope. Haven't found the right one, I guess."

I looked away and smiled.

A sound of pounding, of something slapping against the moistened dirt, echoed.

"Deb! Behind you!"

A grizzly bear was running right for us. I unshouldered my rifle, aimed, and fired. The bear fell.

"Oh dear God." I said, wiping my eyes. "I hated to do that. The poor thing was just confused and hungry."

"You had to. He wasn't coming to be petted."

I stepped closer to the bear and smiled. "Have you ever eaten bear meat before?"

"No."

"You will tonight," I replied, pulling out my knife.

With our stomachs full for the first time in days, we sat quietly around the fire.

"I don't understand this feeling that I have for you, Deb. We just met a few days ago. Yet, I feel like I've known you my whole life. How can that be?"

"We're under trying times. There's uncertainty, and we need each other."

After a short pause, he said, "Deb, I want to kiss you."

I smiled and inched into his open arms. We stared at each other for a moment, then our lips met.

"This is going to sound strange," I whispered, "but I think I love you."

Dave squeezed me tight and whispered, "Those words are music to my ears. I love you too."

Dave suddenly tensed and stared at something behind me. "There's a large snake coming right at us," he whispered. "And it's huge!"

"How far?" I asked.

"About twenty feet."

"Get behind the fire!"

I grabbed a log from the flames and pointed the burning end at the snake. It recoiled, raised its head, and hissed before slithering into the dense brush.

"How many times are you going to save my life?"

We slept close to the fire that night.

"I'm extremely worried," I said as we walked. "Nothing on the radio. No humans in sight. Where is everybody? And look, burnt trees again. We're leaving our little paradise."

"Meteors?"

"Somehow, they missed our little perfect place. We're back in hell."

Dave nodded. "Route 5 should be just ahead. We'll see someone there. It's a busy road."

When we reached Route 5, burnt cars littered a crater-filled road. A few were abandoned, but most contained charred bodies.

"There should be rescue vehicles looking for survivors. No aircraft contrails. Nothing. Where is everybody?" Dave looked dejected.

"A relatively undamaged car. Maybe we can get it started."

A man was slumped over the steering wheel. We pulled him out and placed him near the side of the road. I knelt and said a short prayer.

As I wiped tears from my eyes, I whispered, "I hate to leave him here like this, but we must."

The car started, and we headed south on Route 5, avoiding craters and abandoned vehicles.

"It's about ten miles to Kamloops. There'll be people there."

At Kamloops, Dave slowed the car to a crawl. "This is bad. Kamloops has a population of 90,000. Just burnt buildings. Bodies everywhere."

"I don't think anyone's alive. We need to get to Vancouver."

"Route 5 goes there. It's about a four-hour drive."

I nodded. "We'll find someone alive."

"We need gas," Dave replied. "I can siphon some from these cars."

"There's an ambulance in the ditch," I said. "It'll have flexible tubing."

We were soon on our way to Vancouver with plenty of gas. The four-hour drive turned into an extremely long eight hours. In a few places, the road was almost impassable. By nightfall, we stopped on Lion's Gate Bridge overlooking Vancouver. The city was under water and only a few buildings were visible.

"A tsunami beat us here," I whispered. "I doubt if anyone could have lived through this."

"Deb, we may be the only ones alive."

"Impossible!" I replied. "Let's keep looking. Maybe we can make our way to Seattle. I need to find my parents. I'm so worried."

"Dave squeezed my hand. "My parents passed on years ago. I have a sister living near Seattle. I need to find her too. We need a 4-wheel-drive truck."

The next day, as we sat in our provisioned truck and ready to go, I reached over and tenderly took his hand in mine. "You know, Dave, we've professed our love for each another, and I don't even know your full name. How crazy is that?"

"David Adam Follett. And yours?"

"Deborah Eve Stone."

A sudden thought hit me. I looked at him and smiled. "Adam and Eve? Are you kidding?"

Dave laughed as he placed the truck in gear. Suddenly, a flood of clear understanding fell over us.

I thought about the message I just received from above. I nodded, and as I looked up at the clearing clouds, I said, "It all makes sense now. The rain, your ribs, the bad apples, the snake, our sudden attraction and love, our little paradise that provided us with what we needed, including our miraculous healing. And now our middle names? It's clear that God has chosen us for something important, something special. I just hope we don't disappoint Him this time."

"I understand too, Deb. My advice is to not eat the apples."

"And I'll kill that damn snake next time." I giggled.

We picked up speed and headed south.

An intense, double rainbow glowed above the horizon, guiding our way. I knew for certain that despite all that had happened to us, we were in good, loving hands.

Lynn's Thoughts ...

Adam and Eve ... the first couple. Would God start all over again? Would the human race turn out different? A question many have asked and contemplated from the beginning.

Samuel definitely took Christianity by the horns and pulled it through a grinder with this one. A garden where two souls could heal ... the slithering snake ... a bitter apple ... hmmm.

What moral should we derive from this little tale? When God sends his final blow upon us, that perhaps we should hide in a cave or wait it out in the water?

As I read, not only did I understand the symbolism of the apple and snake, but I could take it a little further. Such as, the cave as the womb and the lake as the birthing water? Perhaps our characters were reborn? But reborn into what, and what trials and tribulations must they endure?

In the end, who are the most saved? The ones who perish, or the ones who remain behind?

As my father always said, when it happens, I hope it hits me right on top of my head ...

Gears and Flowers

Tai An Zhou

The boy always knew how long it would take to get there. It was ten minutes by hoverbike or another five if he walked. If he followed the taller and thicker grass, he would be there in no time. She was watering the garden as usual. Her long, blonde hair was pulled back by the breeze, mimicking a yellow flag that streamed through the sky. He brought flowers, freshly plucked from the riverbank. He didn't know if she would like them but there were so many on his way past the river – reds, greens, and blues in a shimmering display – it seemed like a shame not to pick them, so he did.

He ran when he saw her. He couldn't help himself. So beautiful just standing there, looking calm, almost devoid of motion except for the movement of the watering can. She seemed as much a part of the garden as the flowers, or the bugs, or the sunshine.

But somehow when he arrived, his youthful enthusiasm would fall away, leaving only his shyness behind. He managed a small greeting. "Hi."

She smiled. "Hello." She was a girl – a woman? Something, somewhere in between and of so few words.

She didn't say anything after that. There was no need. He did all the talking, all the running, all the scampering. He rolled through the mud, because unlike the other grownups, she never told him not to. Was she a grownup? He didn't know. He told her stories, some were true, some were made up. Some were about how he and his friends had dug up a secret treasure and buried it somewhere else. Some place where no one would ever find. He told her about how Roy fell off his Dad's hoverbike and everyone laughed. How he was starting school next year and was sure it was going to be great. What he liked best was that she listened. She always smiled and never scolded or lectured or told him what to do or what not to do. She just smiled and watered her garden.

Hours passed and the sky turned from blue to green to gold and finally to the color he liked best, a mix of orange and black and grey. He'd have to leave soon, which he hated, but it was okay because there was always tomorrow. When it was time, he waved *bye* and shot off like a rocket. His shyness forgotten. He would be back tomorrow, and the day after that, at least until the summer was over. Maybe next summer and the one after that. But like all boys, he lived in the moment and had no thought about the morrow. His eyes darted from one wonder to another – the trees, the sky, the clouds. On his way back across the roads, the woman was soon forgotten.

The boy knew the path even though it had changed a bit. The grass no longer grew thick and long, but short and fine. The rains had changed. He owned a new bike and now the minutes were less.

But he still took the time to run along the path to her house. However, he did not stop for flowers. His legs were longer and his body bigger. He ran with a steady movement, feet pounding against the earth, one-two, one-two. It was just the sheer joy of being alive and seeing her.

She was there, not a day older. She watered her garden with the same motions and smiles. The wind was not as strong but still tossed her hair much like he remembered. He lost his train of thought in midsentence, caught in each strand as it flew hither and thither.

He always wondered what she did with her flowers. One day he plucked his courage and asked. The blooms that grew were different from those that were in town. The colors and smells delighted his senses. She answered that she sold them at the markets. He nodded. He didn't think to ask what she did with the money, and she never told him.

He ran back the same way he had come. He would be back the next day and the day after that. Life was simple, life was good.

He grew older and the valley seemed to bloom with more and more life. Perhaps he never noticed before because he was caught inside the stories he told – the blue sky and the wind in her hair. But now he noticed that the flowers grew not only by the bank but by the hillside, and the trees were different each time he came. He was growing older, and as he grew, everything else grew older and bigger.

School was longer and his visits shorter. He no longer ran up the path by the river. Instead, he walked slower more lost in thought. There was more to life now than just visits and flowers and her. His lessons had broadened his world, and he knew about more things, more than just his town and the others around him.

A long time ago, fire and war had split and ravaged the land. Many died, their countries destroyed. Life had changed after the devastation – the valley and stream and trees. Nothing was there before. However, life now grew after many, many years – after the death and terror.

He didn't know what to make of this knew found knowledge. The children at school still laughed and played, and he did those things with them. But something had changed. The boy had been introduced to death. Even if he hadn't seen it himself. He now understood that the world was not always bright and free and clear. Knowledge had transformed him.

But she never changed. She saw him, she smiled, and she listened – and she watered her garden. Different blooms to suit the season, but her green-blue eyes, the same movements, remained. One flower turned into another.

He never told her about what he learned at school, and as always, she never asked. He walked back the same way he had come, and this time he didn't look at the flowers or the trees or the sky. He felt better. He always felt better when he saw her. But still, there remained an unease. He didn't know what to make of it, and so he just continued to walk.

The boy approached the bank somewhat carelessly now. He was in no hurry. But his hoverbike was a newer model, and he could fly so close that he didn't have to walk very far. By now, he understood that she wasn't like other girls. Her hair never grew longer. She wasn't like his mother or his sister or the girls at his school. She treated him the same, year after year, whereas others seemed to treat him differently. Was this what growing up was like?

She was different. Different from anyone he knew. And yet she was always the same, always smiling, always listening, never far from the garden. He didn't know what it was that made her different and for some reason he found that he didn't care.

The stories he told now were different. He spoke about the future. About what he would do when school was over and with the days to come. There were boats by the river that needed fixing. After all, hoverbikes never worked on water. Old Man Jacob was always talking about how they should do something about the houses abandoned near the coast. Maybe next year they could visit the city, and then –

And then, and then, and then. What had always been a place for the present suddenly became the future, filled with things to come. There were more than the houses and the valley. There were worlds that only existed in dreams and in words. But she listened all the same, as she always had. And smiled and asked questions. How do you fix the boats? How far is the city? When are you getting a new bike?

They spoke for what seemed like hours, and when the time came for him to leave, he dragged his feet, finding just one more question to ask and one last answer to hear. He knew eventually he would have to leave and no matter how hard he tried to push off that reality, the sky would still darken and the night would still fall. He had to leave.

It was on an autumn evening while running across the stream, that he realized he loved her. He always had, ever since he was a young boy. And with that realization, the trees and flowers and the world took on a whole new meaning. He looked up at the star-sprinkled night's sky and couldn't recall a happier time.

He ran along the stream as he always did, but not for a long time. And this time he carried flowers, picked from the hill instead of by the stream. It would take him longer to get there without the hoverbike but it didn't matter, he would just run. He didn't want to spoil the flowers, and if he rode his bike, they would be carried away by the exhaust.

He didn't know how to ask what he was going to ask. He had turned the words over in his mind a hundred times, no, a thousand. It seemed like the best idea in the world, and then seconds later, the worst. But he had to ask. The path he had walked so many times before now seemed long and unfamiliar. The pebbles and stones strewn here and there were strangers to him as he slowly made his way to the familiar house.

She was there as always, watering the flowers.

He took a deep breath, plucked up his courage and spoke the words. "If you would ... if you would go with me to the dance?"

She smiled and shook her head.

He felt torn. He was sure she would say yes. He knew she would not say no. Now, he didn't know what he thought or thought he had thought. He just knew that he had to ask and that he would be prepared for whatever she might say.

Turning around so she couldn't see his tears, he aimed for home. He thought that maybe he could have asked it differently or said it better. But maybe he couldn't and she would have said no regardless. He thought that – no, he couldn't think of anything. Except how disappointed he felt. He glanced over his shoulder and she was looking at him, still smiling, flowers in her hands.

The man had not been back for many years. There was no need. He didn't know why he was walking along the same path he had walked so many times before. It took only five minutes to get there now. The new hoverbikes with boosters were stronger to pass the thicker foliage. He thought of taking the scenic route but decided against it. He just didn't have the time to spare.

He had grown since the last time he was here. He knew she was different. In the city, or rather in Iverness, they spoke of relics found from the war. Maybe she was one of them – a relic. He wasn't sure what she was, but he was working on it. Somehow, it didn't matter what she was or was not. He wanted to apologize. He walked away when he shouldn't have, and it was time to make amends.

He stepped up to the house. The flowers looked different this year. He hadn't seen them for some time. The difference in colors were amazing. And – she was there, waiting.

He looked into her eyes. "I'm sorry."

She smiled. "It's okay."

The day passed. Studying her in the evening sunlight, he wondered about her smile. Why was she always smiling? How could she smile? The time for stories and questions and answers had passed, so he simply closed his eyes and took his leave. The way back seemed shorter than he remembered, or maybe it was just that his legs were longer.

It had been some time again, but not as long as the last. He parked his bike where he always parked and walked the rest of the way for old times' sake. The valley was beautiful in the fall. This time, he took the time to notice the colors and shades of every bloom and leaf as the dappled light of autumn bathed through the clouds. He would not return for some time, and he wanted to commit everything to memory. Not that he ever would. He ignored the voice that told him he might never return. He would – he would. He just didn't know when.

The road leading to the house had changed since the last time he was there. It was longer than he remembered. Seemed to wind on forever, crossing the rivers and streams that he knew he should know but didn't. Memory was a fickle thing, and the man was learning that.

He stepped up to the house and she was there. There were less bushes now and less flowers. But she was still watering as always. There was no wind, and her hair did not flutter in the breeze. He approached her, slowly.

"I'm getting married," he said. "I'd like you to be at my wedding." It was easier to say than he thought. He had rehearsed the question a few times, unlike his last disastrous request.

"I can't leave the garden," she replied.

He knew that she would say that and it hurt. But she was smiling and that made it a little easier to accept.

"I won't come back for some time," he said.

She nodded as if she already knew.

They spent time staring at each other. He wanted to tell her everything, just like he had as a young boy – about his wife-to-be, about the house they were buying, about the move they were going to make. But he didn't say anything. He just stood there, staring, as the fall leaves swirled around them.

She smiled as he turned to leave. On the way back, he passed flowers that he didn't know, and trees that were much, much taller than he remembered. His eyes darted to and fro as they had many years ago. He tried to lose himself in every detail. He was caught up in his memories and didn't notice that he had arrived at his bike. He mounted in a swift motion and headed for home.

"Daddy, Daddy, you're too slow!"

There were two sets of footprints along the wooded trails now – one large and one small.

Nothing else had changed much. It seemed that time had stopped. He had grown older and wiser and sadder, but the valley seemed somehow locked in time. He made his way along the road, his son skipping ahead.

Halfway to the house he stopped and realized that things were different. Drones were flittering around the trees, pruning and watering. The changed weather was easy enough to spot, and the flowers' blooms seemed richer. Technology had worked its magic and had improved this sanctuary. He wasn't sure if he was happy or not at the way things were, and so he treaded the same path with a little doubt and confusion.

She was there as usual, but not watering the plants. She was waiting for him. How she knew he would be coming he had no idea. He stared at her as his young son pranced around, much as he had so many years ago. The boy shrieked as he ran through the flowers that never looked more beautiful.

She stared at him, smiling. He felt that the world could end, and she would still be there for him. Her hair blew in the wind like always, and he was taken back to a time long ago. He didn't know what to say. Perhaps he didn't need to say anything. He opened his mouth but his son barreled through his legs, and he hit the ground, knocking the wind out of him.

She laughed. She had never laughed before.

Smiling sheepishly, he stood, brushing grass from his legs. He took his son's hand and said goodbye.

She nodded.

The way home was just as long as he remembered. He took the time to enjoy the trees, pointing out the names of every flower and leaf and delighting in his son's exuberant cries. The sky spread out above them, a clear and distant blue, and as he stooped to boost the young boy onto his back, he could not recall ever feeling happier.

The paths had all been washed away by the floods. There was no safe place for him to walk, but it didn't matter. The exhaust of the bike glowed a cool green as it sailed easily above the rocky ground. His hoverbike made a gentle landing. He didn't have to move a finger. He had finished the alterations a year ago, and now he could operate it remotely. Its control was refined enough to make it to the deepest part of the valley, skirting the fallen foliage that the rains dislodged.

The house was gone. So was the garden. It had been too many years since, and people had moved away long before nature finished the job that man had started. The old man walked slowly to where he knew she was. He had to walk slowly at his age. In his condition he could only move one short step at a time, and so he hobbled to where she waited.

She stood quietly as she always did.

He raised his trembling hand. "I just want you to know that ... that ..." he couldn't finish his thought.

She took his hand. Her blonde hair flowing in the breeze. Her green-blue eyes were the same hue that he had admired as a child. He didn't actually need to say anything for she knew. She would understand as she always did. At his age, he knew all about her. Or thought he did. After twenty years, the satellite links were up and running, and the orbital archives were now accessible. He read manuals, watched holodisks, and talked to all the experts. None could explain her and nothing explained her smile. He didn't know why he had made the long trip back, other than he had to see her one last time. Even with the implants, he knew he wouldn't last long, not at his age. And that was why he came back.

He stared at her and she smiled. He had millions of things to tell her. About how they finally terraformed the areas that were devastated by the war. How his wife had taken ill and died. About how his son and daughter had moved to the cities and were now scientists like him. How they found other androids, but none that looked or acted like her.

And this time it was the simple fragility of his body that rendered him speechless. He opened his mouth but all that escaped was a shallow cough, and then another, and another. He collapsed, and she gently knelt, holding his aging frame that was now racked by shudders and jerks. When all quieted, he looked up. She was smiling.

BEGINNING TECHNICAL READOUT AND ANALYSIS . . .

SUBJECT: A-1, OLDER MALE . . .

SUBJECT REQUIRES ATTENTION – CHECKING PRIMARY OBJECTIVES . . .

PRIMARY OBJECTIVE: PLANTS WATERED – FLOWERS COLLECTED – FULFILLED . . .

SECONDARY OBJECTIVE: RESPOND TO SUBJECT'S QUERIES – FULFILLED . . .

TRINARY OBJECTIVE: LISTEN TO SUBJECT – FULFILLED . . .

UNIT HAS FULFILLED ALL OBJECTIVES – AWAITING FURTHER INSTRUCTIONS . . .

Lynn's Thoughts …

AI - artificial intelligence … how will it evolve? I really enjoyed this story. How the world progressed round the female robot that never once left her home. The only thing I couldn't understand was why the robot that was obviously assigned to the boy/man remained so far away. I saw the boy finding the AI on one of his explorations of the hillsides and then visiting on a regular basis. But in the end, the AI stated that her objective was to listen and respond to his queries.

Did the boy's parents leave the AI there for him to find? Was the AI living in his grandparents' aging house? So many unanswered questions.

Our author's depiction of the future and how it will develop around us is an interesting concept. Because we do that now. We are so distracted by our daily lives (the old house) that we fail to see how the world is changing (the environment). We then become that female robot simply existing between today and tomorrow. At least, until the end arrives, and we await further instructions.

Getting Out

Bruce Neuburger

Fritz had closed the wooden crate and hit the last nail one final time when the doorbell buzzed.

Anna who had stood watching her son, her eyes tearing, walked over to the living room window. “It’s the movers, Fritz.”

Fritz huffed and jogged down the stairs to the door that opened onto Trogerstrasse street. He blinked at the bright sunlight that reflected in the foyer. It was an unusually warm day in Munich even for July. A stocky man wearing a short-sleeved, blue shirt, matching pants, and a docker’s cap stood patiently outside. Sweat beaded on his forehead. Fritz noticed a thin line trickling down the side of his face. The man looked vaguely familiar, but Fritz couldn’t recall where he’d seen him before.

“You have something for me, no?” the man asked.

Fritz and the mover climbed the stairs to apartment three. Just inside the door was a wooden crate that held several items of furniture.

"This it?" the man asked.

"Yes," Fritz replied. "You'll be taking it to the train."

"Yeah, of course." The mover leaned down, shoving the box onto the hand cart. "You can sign the papers tomorrow if you wish."

"I'm sorry?" Fritz asked.

"You have to come to the warehouse ... sign the papers. It's just routine. When someone's leaving the country. A bureaucratic thing. Don't worry, it's just routine."

Fritz glanced at his father, Benno, who had stepped out of the bedroom. "Just routine," Fritz repeated, responding to his father's concerned look.

"You've got to sign the papers before we can load it on the train," the mover added, reaching for the door. "Nothing to worry about, Mr. Neuburger." The man closed the door behind him.

The following morning, Fritz and his friend, Frank Mittelberger, drove to the warehouse where their items were held before being loaded onto the train. Both had received their affidavits from relatives in the U.S. along with their precious visas. They were leaving. Although their ships were to depart from different ports on different days, they were leaving Munich together by train on July 28th, 1938. First, however, they had to sign the papers at the warehouse.

"What do you think this paper signing is all about?" Fritz asked.

"Don't know. Surprised me too," Frank replied. "But I think we'll be okay. I recognized the rep from the moving company. I've seen him at the synagogue. He was pretty reassuring that everything will be fine."

"He said it was routine." Fritz maneuvered his Opel carefully through the Munich traffic.

"Of course." Frank nodded. "Fucking with Jews from every possible angle is *just* routine. They have a special bureau for that, don't they? The Reich bureau of assholes for special measures to fuck Jews."

"For the Fatherland," Fritz added. "Part of the great new opportunities our glorious leader has brought to our beloved Fatherland!"

"We opened up and will continue to open up, for our sacred Aryan volk … great new Jew fucking opportunities in our new Germany!" Frank stated imitating Hitler's frantic style of speech.

They rolled their eyes.

Frank and Fritz had been friends for years. In 1933, they founded a Jewish sports club in Munich. Prior to that, they were members of Munich's 1860 Club, well known throughout Germany as one of the premier sporting associations. For Frank and Fritz, sports were both a passion and a refuge from their daily lives. For Fritz, it was a welcome diversion from his job as a traveling salesman. For Frank, it was a distraction from his career in engineering. As 1860 members, they spent their free time working or hanging out with other members from their respective teams. Fritz was on the track and handball teams. Frank was a well-regarded soccer player. Although they competed in their respective sports and moved in different circles, both were steeped in the traditions of Munich sports, especially, the post competition beer drinking. Beer, after all, Fritz often insisted and only half in jest, was an essential part of any true Munich athlete's training.

Prior to 1933, neither associated much with other Jews except family members. Nor were they religious. Their Judaism consisted of an occasional visit to a Munich synagogue, usually during the *High Holidays* of Rosh Hashana and Yom Kippur, though both had been Bar Mitzvahed.

On January 30, 1933, Adolf Hitler was sworn in as Germany's new chancellor, and a new word entered prominently in the national vocabulary – *Gleichshaltung*. *Gleichshaltung* signified the Nazi intent to reshape Germany's political, social, and cultural life to form a racialized view of history and society. For Jews it meant being shunned by their country. Newspapers often remarked about the coming laws that would set Germany on a new path. In the Nazi press, this was about the realization of the promise to a new national greatness. There were criticisms in the opposition press to the changes with its heavy emphasis on racial definitions and divisions, but those critics were coming under assault. These oppositional news organizations were vilified by the Nazis and sometimes attacked physically, as *lugenpresse* – lying media.

The day after Fritz returned to Munich from an extended sales trip to the northern German cities in March of 1933, Fritz visited the 1860 sports center, looking forward to working out and seeing his friends. He'd read the news of the new policy while on the road, but the sign at the door still staggered him. In bold letters that mimicked Hebrew script was written:

Juden Zutritt Verboten!
Jews not allowed!

Opinions among the 1860 members were divided. A few of his teammates and others in the sports club were openly hostile to the change, calling it *Nazi bullshit.* Others said they would quit in protest. But nothing ever came of their threats. More fell more quietly in line with the new policy. Even those outraged by the new laws openly expressed their displeasure to their now expelled fellow athletes, holding back in front of anyone they didn't trust. Most of all, they kept quiet while in public. As a consequence, a new normalcy set in.

With Germany's Jews now excluded from sports clubs and other associations, new Jewish associations formed. That's how Fritz and Frank came to be among the founding members of the Munich Jewish Sports Club. And it was at this point that they started hanging out together.

During the years he spent on the road with Thormann and Dannhäuser sports shoe company and later with Julius Levy, a sports clothing company, Fritz became acquainted with the small business owners and other salespeople in the towns and cities he visited. He enjoyed good relations with them, and they treated him well. But after 1933, as with his former teammates, attitudes began to change. Even among those who expressed progressive views and acceptance of other cultures, religions, and so forth, Nazi racial attitudes began to influence their thinking.

Outspoken anti-Nazis grew subdued. Some, who identified as Social Democrats and had sympathies toward communism, began to back-peddle, to *reevaluate* their views on Hitler and his new regime. There were those who apologized for this, arguing, "You have to take the bad with the good." The new racial laws were harmful and unjust, they affirmed, but now there was the improved economy and a renewal of *national pride*. The country was showing its defiance in the face of the highly unpopular Versailles accords. "These had to be considered," they said.

In Fritz's first years as a traveling salesman, which began in 1927, religion had not been much of an issue. Some knew he was Jewish, some not, but for most, it didn't matter. His customers and salesmen friends, particularly in the northern cities, regarded Fritz as a pleasant, enthusiastic, and hardworking sales rep with luminous green eyes, and a funny Bavarian accent.

After 1933 however, Fritz steered clear of discussions of religion and politics. Despite this, he often became party to conversations which were, to say the least, uncomfortable. There were those who had formerly been uninterested in religion, but had suddenly become overnight experts on Jews and Judaism. "Jews," they would say, "were the cause of Germany's problems." Jews had manipulated the economy to favor themselves. Jews were the main instigators of a culture that was degrading the country, inducing immorality, and undermining patriotism. Jews were encouraging sexual deviance and an unhealthy turn from the *tradition*, by which they often meant that women no longer played the obedient and subservient roles expected in the *ideal* German family. In short, Jews were behind everything others found unpleasant or not in conformity with the *new* Germany that the Nazi regime was bringing into being, and that many Germans in the middle class were falling in line with. Fritz felt increasingly uncomfortable and unwelcome.

Once, he made the mistake of accepting an invitation to have a beer with a customer whose views he already knew he did not share. After a few glasses, his drinking partner became agitated.

"Jews," he had stated, "I don't know if you know them well … but I do. I can tell you, Fritz. The Jews …" – he leaned uncomfortably close and his voice grew annoyingly loud – "… fucked us in the war. While our German boys were suffering in the trenches … getting their arms blown off, getting their balls blown off, the Jews were at home safe and becoming rich. And the degenerate bastards were fucking our women while their husbands were dying on the front!"

This was, to say the least, an unpleasant and frightening moment, as his drinking partner seemed interested in, not only loudly proclaiming his profound indignation, but on having Fritz join his little hate fest. Fritz had to hold himself back from the impulse to either get up and storm out or take his beer and smash it into the face of this inebriated, ignorant fool. Both of which would have had disastrous consequences.

Yet, he longed to respond to the lies. He wanted to talk about how his father, well past fighting age, served as a guard at the Dachau weapons depot, or about the twelve-thousand German Jews that died serving in the war, or the tens of thousands more that were injured, including several of his uncles. He wanted to talk about how his family, once prosperous, had lost nearly everything by investing in German war bonds and through the cataclysmic inflation in the aftermath of war. And how because of that, as a teenager, he had to work to keep his family fed.

He could not talk about the bitter irony that German Jews were, in some ways, the most ardent supporters of the war. As people historically discriminated against, they went to extra lengths to prove their loyalty. But it was also because one of Germany's enemies was Russia. Czarist Russia was a notoriously hellish place for Jews. Fritz had picked up bits and pieces of this history from his mother who, before the war, had gotten to know Russian Jews in Munich who'd fled Czarist pogroms – the anti-Jewish riots. There were strong anti-Czarist sentiments that played into the Jewish attitudes toward the war that made German Jews even more partisan to the German imperialist cause.

But Fritz said nothing about this. Daring to express such ideas publicly after 1933 was a great risk. Therefore, he remained quiet and listened as the newly born experts on Jews and racial matters spouted the talking points that the collaborating or cowed German media propagated. Such experiences shook him from his stubborn belief that, as bad as things were, he and others like him could probably ride out the storm because, at the end of the day, they were as German as anyone.

But by the spring of 1937, Fritz was gathering the paperwork needed for a visa application to the U.S. His sister, Hani, who had emigrated in the fall of 1937, assisted with the needed affidavit. By the beginning of 1938, he was more than ready to leave his homeland. He was making preparations when word came that his employer, the Jewish-owned company Thormann and Dannhäuser, was being forced out of business and taken over by the new *Aryan* owners.

Frank, like Fritz, had held stubbornly for some time to the idea that the upsurge in anti-Semitism was like a virus that would burn itself out. He was an engineer who made it into one of Germany's premier science schools, the Technical University of Munich. But his path forward after 1933 had narrowed. By 1938, it was clear he would never be able to practice his profession in Germany.

Now they were both leaving. They were ready, even though the cost weighed heavily, especially the emotional burden of leaving their families behind. For Fritz it was his parents and cousins and aunts and uncles. Life without them was hard to imagine.

In the process of being approved to leave, the two émigrés had to submit detailed lists of their possessions down to the last item of clothing. And they had to pay a tax on everything being shipped. It was straight up plunder by a corrupt German fascist state, but they had no choice. They were only allowed to take a few things, besides their clothes, in one wooden crate. Everything had to be declared and paid for. Since they could take no money, both had splurged on their transportation. Each bought a first-class berth on their respective ships, something they otherwise would not have done, which meant they were traveling above their respective classes.

Fritz confided to his friend that he had placed several undeclared cameras rolled in the carpet his parents urged him to take as a remembrance from their apartment. He had also hidden a few gold coins inside a sock. Frank barely reacted when he heard this. He was suddenly in a more somber mood. He kept his gaze focused on the familiar sights of Munich that passed by his window.

At the warehouse the two émigrés were escorted by a worker to their packed boxes and told to wait. While they waited, they joked about things they'd heard about New York.

"I'm told that in New York you have to be careful about large apes climbing buildings," Fritz said, laughing in a mock seriousness.

"I'd rather take my chances with those apes than the ones running things here," Frank countered in a low voice.

Fritz was about to reply but stopped. He felt his body freeze as a uniformed Nazi approached. The pounding in his chest became so strong, he thought it would make a noticeable sound. The two would-be émigrés glanced at each other. Fritz bit his lower lip, trying to look relaxed as the officer stepped closer.

The Nazi was a tall man who seemed to be about forty. He wore a dark green uniform with a gold cross of the old Reich on his dark necktie. On his cap was the Nazi eagle and a Swastika in its talons. His voice was anything but friendly. "You're here to sign papers for the possessions you're shipping?"

They nodded.

The officer listed the rules. "You will have to sign off on these restrictions. And you'll need to open those boxes for me."

Fritz felt his blood drain from his head. But he kept a straight, calm face. A worker who'd accompanied the inspector, handed Frank a crowbar. With a rough jerk, he pried open the lid of his small wooden box.

The Nazi looked at the papers again. He pushed up his cap before bending over to peer inside. He reached down and pulled up a bundle, wrapped in what looked like a tablecloth. He opened the cloth revealing a half dozen framed photos. The inspector poked through the stack, lifting a few items. He then returned to the crate, placing his hand onto the neatly folded linen. He felt within the crevices of the linen, his arm disappearing into the box. The inspector looked up at Frank and nodded. "You're leaving from Hamburg?" the Nazi asked, looking back at the paper. "And you," he said, looking over at Fritz.

Fritz opened his box, revealing a small night table with its legs wrapped in cloth and next to it a rolled-up carpet. He didn't dare look at Frank, who instinctively took a half step back.

"Let's see that, what? Table?"

Fritz pulled the small end table, from the box. It was made from walnut, with a drawer and cabinet underneath. Its curved legs were adorned with rounded feet. It had sat by his bed for years, his favorite piece of furniture. He placed it on the floor.

The inspector looked inside the drawer and the opened the cabinet. Then he looked back into the box at the carpet and pushed it to one side. His cap nearly fell off before he pushed it back onto his head, compensating the awkwardness of the gesture with an exaggerated stern tone, "Both escaping to the United States ..." He looked at the documents in his hand and then over at Frank and Fritz. "You Jews don't like Germany!?" It was hard to tell if this was a question or an assertion.

Fritz shrugged.

"You're leaving from Le Havre. You have a first-class berth on an English Cunard ship, Georgic," the inspector stated.

At least the idiot can read, Fritz thought to himself.

"Why not a German ship?" the inspector asked with an accusing tone.

Fritz bit his lip again but stopped. His heart, beating so hard he thought it might just push its way out of his chest.

"Juden," the inspector said, drawing out the word, with an exaggerated emphasis on the first syllable. "Always travel first class … hmm." The inspector stared at Fritz, like he was trying to think of something else to say – something damning. "If I had my way, it would be different." He glared at Fritz and then again at Frank. After a short pause, he turned, took a few steps, tossing the documents at the open box. The papers hit the edge and scattered on the ground. The inspector gestured to the worker. "Bring the signed documents back to me." The officer walked away.

Fritz and Frank signed the papers and checked the appropriate boxes, indicating they obeyed the various obligations and restrictions for travel out of Germany – obligations they had already sworn to in order to have their passports approved. In wielding the pen, their hands were remarkably steady, defying the turmoil broiling deep inside.

Inside the car, it was Frank who broke the silence. "I guess we missed our chance to see Dachau."

"Looked like we were about to have a free trip," Fritz replied.

"It's always free for Jews, Fritz."

Fritz frowned at his friend, "That was a foolish thing I did, hiding the money. I'm sorry."

"Don't worry," Frank replied. "I'm sure it's not the last foolish thing you or I will ever do. At least you'll have a camera. You can take pictures and send them to the inspector as a *thank you.*"

"I didn't expect the asshole to be there."

"Yeah. Didn't that moving guy say this was just some routine bureaucratic thing?"

"He didn't say a goddamn thing about an inspection," Fritz added, bitterly. "He must have known. Didn't you say he was Jewish?"

"Yeah. I guess it's like they say, snakes come in all colors."

Lynn's Thoughts ...

What a relevant story ... especially with the political atmosphere heating up around us. So much history hidden within the folds of time. If only we could unravel and fully grasp what did or did not happen. Who said, 'History was written by the victors.'?

We often say that the statement is from Winston Churchill, but he only borrowed it. The actual origins are unknown. That also means that much of our history is unknown. If you ask a couple why they divorced, I'm sure you will have three stories, his ... hers ... and the truth.

We could write our own history and place it in a time capsule. Then a trillion years from now someone would find it. They'd open it and say, "Oh look, that building is called a hospital and it was used to store canned goods!"

Yep, sometimes I think we're nothing more than canned goods. All sealed up and stuck on a shelf.

Thank you, Bruce, for reliving the past and bringing a little hope to an otherwise dreary environment.

Into the Light

Jerry Aveta

He was running late and wanted this day to be perfect. He had traveled this route many times as a child in the back seat of the family station wagon but that was years ago. Nothing looked familiar and neither did the traffic.

"Get here when you get here," was her response when he texted about his tardiness.

Whew, at least she's not ticked off at me, he thought as he sat, simmering at the endless stream of red lights.

The casual lunch was scheduled after an almost fifty-year break since their last encounter. They were reunited through the wonders of social media available to any bored office worker as was his circumstance. After initial email exchanges, ensuring they hadn't forgotten one another, phone calls and texts on an ever-increasing basis, they planned this physical reunion. As he parked outside her office, he noticed his palms were sweaty, and he had butterflies in his stomach. He felt like a teenager again.

They were from two different life experiences when they had met in a physics class during their final year of high school. She had lived on four different continents before she was ten years old, and he had lived in the same house from preschool until the time they met. Her father was in the State Department, which took her family from Washington D.C. to Germany to the West Indies to Canada to New Jersey. His dad, the son of an immigrant, dropped out of school in the eighth grade and survived the African and Italian campaigns of WWII as an Army medic. His dad met his mom when he gave his seat to her on a crowded train while on leave from the Army. Her dad and mom met on VE Day during a street celebration in Paris. It was probably those same romantic spirits that they inherited from their parents that led the high school sweethearts to reconnect many years later.

What they did not know was that each had experienced a few very dark days since they last saw each other. They would soon learn their stories as time passed. They would listen to each other's pain and in so doing would help each other to heal. What they didn't know was that they were preparing themselves to experience a few additional dark days, only this time, together.

She had married in her mid-twenties, had three children, and lived through the horrible experience of losing her son to an accidental drug overdose when he was only twenty-five. Trying to describe her journey through those dark days and the subsequent dismantling of a forty-year marriage was not the subject of this writing. Those details are for her to tell, in her time, in her way.

His adult life was quite different. In comparison, by his mid-twenties he had married and become a parent. Shortly after his divorce, his ex-wife died in a car accident in the mountains of West Virginia on Christmas Eve. He learned of the fatal accident upon his Christmas morning arrival in West Virginia but hadn't known if his daughter was also in the car. One can imagine the emotional release when he discovered his daughter was safe at her aunt's house. All were awaiting his arrival so he could explain to his daughter the death of her mother. Summoning the words and the manner to broach the subject escaped him. He was content to just hold her until she asked about her mommy. He was surprised how easily he found the right words at the right moment.

He left his northern Virginia apartment alone and returned as a single parent of a three-year-old. He had little knowledge of little girls. He had no sisters. He'd only been married a few short years before divorcing, and most of that time was childless. Those early days of single parenting were pure survival, making it through with the use of Hamburger Helper and occasional baby-sitting from his mother. Each day was a challenge but filled with gratitude for having his daughter in his life.

Three years later, he met and married a divorcee who had two daughters, one the same age as his daughter and one about to turn thirteen. He thought it was a great arrangement. A playmate for his daughter, a built-in babysitter for the younger girls, and a woman who could cook. Needless to say, he was a little naïve about the dynamics of a blended family with three children of three different fathers. It wasn't long before the dysfunction became clear, even to him.

He was inadequately equipped to deal with the relational dynamics of stepchildren and stepparents while trying to deal with the natural child-parent relationships, all blended into the same family. There were competing priorities. No matter how much one tried, there were always a bias or favoring toward one's natural child compared to a stepchild. Likewise, regardless how close the stepchild became to the stepparent, inevitably the stepchild would one day announce, "You're not my father!" He could attest to that experience.

Additionally, there was the dynamic of his wife's ex-spouse trying to parent his child sporadically and chaotically in this new blended family. Any given day of the week, there were bound to be one or more crises percolating through the household. These were some of the challenges involved in fashioning a resemblance to a functional family life.

After the wedding, he discovered his wife's excessive drinking. It wasn't long after that he discovered her tendency toward infidelity. Confronted with the possibility of going through another divorce so early in his new marriage he did something that he had never done before. He cried out to God in desperation. He had no idea that God would take him up on his invitation. God entered into his circumstance and gave him the help he desperately needed to be the father and husband required for this relationship tornado.

He described the next thirty years as a faith journey. Being raised a Catholic and sent to parochial school for his first eight grades, he was comfortable with the concept of faith being a part of the family's social architecture. He avoided recruitment into the Catholic priesthood in the sixth grade because of his parents' emotional reaction against a commitment at such a young age. He came to realize that it was God's grace that saved him from such a mistake. Only God could know that this Catholic child would eventually become a Protestant Pentecostal pastor. He would have never made it as a Catholic priest.

Late one night after a difficult evening, he was alone in his bedroom when he requested God to intervene in his family. That night started as a social engagement with a few friends. There was excessive drinking, subsequent arguing, and a late-night call to his father-in-law requesting intervention. By the next day, his passionate plea to God was dismissed until weeks later.

The event was a business weekend held at a resort in Pennsylvania. A convenient non-denominational Christian service was offered to the conference attendees on Sunday before their departure. A friend, who was speaking that morning, invited him and his family to attend the service. His friend had a successful career in government, an Italian heritage, was raised Catholic like him, and was well respected among their common professional associates.

He had been to Protestant services before, which were quite different from those in the Catholic church. After a moving testimony, his friend asked the audience to invite God into their lives. He was conflicted because he sincerely believed God was already in his life. He didn't believe that more demonstration of that fact was necessary, but he wanted to support his friend in some manner. Feeling conflicted, all he could do was utter a simple prayer, *'God help me.'* He had no explanation for what happened next. He literally felt transported to the front of the room where his friend was standing. They embraced and he wept uncontrollably. When he finally stopped crying, something inside him had changed.

Beginning in college, he routinely contended with an anger deep inside him. It was a slow burn, ready to be revealed with an explosion of emotion in moments of stress. For the most part it stayed hidden in the recesses of his soul, others unaware of its existence or that it was a source of great anxiety. That day, after embracing his friend, the anger was gone and replaced with a deep feeling of peace and joy. At the time, he was facing severe financial stresses with no apparent solutions. The relationships in his family continued to be strained. In spite of these issues, he walked away from the service with an internal assurance that everything would be alright. He didn't know how or why, just that it was going to work out somehow.

There are many scriptures that describe the transformation of a life through faith. His favorite was found in Peter's first epistle where it described God calling us, '*Out of darkness into His marvelous light.*' (1 Peter 2:9) That was the way he felt after that Sunday morning service in Pennsylvania. For the first time his internal darkness was removed, and he was thrust into the light of God that provided peace and joy like no other. His faith journey had begun, unannounced and without warning. He would soon find that his journey would be highlighted by many similar events like that initial one. He would learn to characterize them as the intersection of the natural (us) with the supernatural (God). It was similar to a tornado, which was the intersection of the natural with the unnatural, where the landscape of that intersection was changed in an instant. An intersection of the natural and the supernatural when the landscape of one's faith was changed to a faith-based on experience with God and not just information about God.

His friend who was speaking that impactful Sunday morning was also instrumental in the redirection of his faith away from Catholicism. His friend had transitioned into a Baptist congregation from his Catholic tradition, and it seemed like a logical first step to follow his friend's lead in his new journey of faith. The church provided a structure for his entire family. There were separate ministries for the children and teens, which provided their children with an important peer social structure. At the same time there was a selection of adult ministries for men, women, and married couples. He found an umbrella of instruction and accountability for each member of his family at a time when it was desperately needed. Through this instruction, his family achieved a sense of normalcy in its daily functionality. Consequently, he was able to dive into a structured study of his newly found faith consisting of Sunday classes and more formal studies during the week. Eventually, he earned a Master of Arts in religion and counseling from Liberty University and became deeply involved in teaching and counseling within the church.

His faith grew in knowledge through his various studies and in experience of teaching and counseling others. However, instrumental to his faith journey was the continuation of those intersections between the natural and the supernatural. These experiences changed the understanding of his faith, enabling him to move first from Catholic to Baptist (non-Pentecostal Protestant) then to Assembly of God (Pentecostal Protestant). The journey continued until he became a licensed, ordained minister in the International Pentecostal Holiness Church, finally starting and pastoring his own church for seven years.

While ministering at one of the local churches, his pastor asked him to take on an additional duty. He was asked to counsel a minister who had recently been removed from his pastorate due to infidelity. The suspended minister and his wife attended his class and were counseled as part of the minister's restoration to the denomination to which they belonged. He and the former pastor spent many hours talking and soon became friends. In one of their sessions the suspended minister was asked how he could preach and teach in front of his congregation while he knowingly was doing wrong. His answer was that he would confess his sin to God every week and feel forgiven in order to effectively minister on Sunday, but then would continue in his infidelity during the following week. The minister would repeat this cycle each week until he was caught. He found that logic perplexing and wondered how anyone in the ministry could fool themselves in that way for a continued period of time. Ironically, years later, he would find himself in a similar predicament.

After being delivered into the light that Sunday morning almost thirty years ago, he now found himself in a very dark place. He had closed his church, left his denomination, and was drained of his faith. Sunday mornings would come, and he was more interested in playing golf than attending church. He was recovering from two major surgeries, and on the eve of returning to work, he discovered a sexually explicit email from his wife to her lover.

Where is God now? he thought.

The rage and bitterness consumed him as he prepared for the legal battles that lay ahead, and the financial unraveling of a thirty-year marriage. The Commonwealth of Virginia did not levy consequences for infidelity in the divorce settlement that was solely subsidized by him. His spouse had not worked for many years and therefore was interpreted not to have any liability in spite of her acts. It was a simple numerical calculation that prorated the retirement he had earned between both parties based on the number of years married. It was referred to as a no-fault divorce because his wife did not have independent means. The only condition that would alter the calculation was in the event that his wife remarried. A consideration rejected by her and her live-in boyfriend because they did not want to jeopardize their income.

He'd been faithful during his marriage but felt that paying the consequences for his divorce was an abandonment by God. Especially, after devoting most of his adult life in service to his faith. Who wouldn't?

Two critical events happened. First, was the reconnection with his high school sweetheart. It was ironic they were reconnecting when both were experiencing similar circumstances. Because of his bitterness, he was not willing to admit that God was involved. That his life was his doing alone, at least that was the way it felt. They leaned on each other and helped each other to heal. The second occurred when he felt he needed therapy. He was recommended to a local professional and diligently met with him twice a week for months. The first event restored his heart. The second was instrumental in pushing him back on the path to his faith.

Counseling was cathartic. There was nothing said or done that was particularly innovative, but the therapist validated that his anger was justified, which helped but did nothing to alleviate his bitterness. He knew his anger was a spiritual problem invading his soul, and the only solution was forgiveness. He had taught and counseled this spiritual principle many times throughout the years. But he could not go there now. He wasn't going to forgive anyone who had hurt and taken advantage of him. However, that all changed.

He could never recall what was discussed in the counseling session that day, but he did discover the besetting issue causing his bitterness. His daughter had been abused with indifference from her stepmother and indirectly from him. Her stepmother gave little affection while over giving attention to her own children. His daughter's bedroom was next to her stepsister's, and night after night, she would listen to his ex-wife spend quality time with her daughter and then walk past his daughter's bedroom without acknowledgment. This type of rejection was manifested in different ways at various times. He would confront his ex-wife behind closed doors, but it would escalate into bitter arguments, each accusing the other of neglecting each other's children. It was a no-win situation, and he gave up trying to solve the problem.

He tried to make it up to his daughter in other ways but there was no substitute for a mother's love, or in his daughter's case a surrogate stepmom, no matter how hard he tried. A stepmother can never be the equivalent of a natural mother. But what he didn't realize was the devastating effects a stepmother's rejection could have on a child. To this day his daughter, by her own admission, still covets the approval of her former stepmom.

That day in counseling, he felt the extent of the pain he had caused his daughter by not fighting for her well-being, shaking him to the core of his soul. So much so, that he sat in his car and openly wept, unable to drive. He called his daughter and asked for forgiveness.

"Of course, Dad," she said as she cried.

He wept again, this time with his daughter. It was a healing for them. A forgiveness that was needed to expel the bitterness he was harboring. He didn't need to forgive others, he just had to ask his daughter for her forgiveness. Over the years, he lived oblivious to his own hypocrisy while ministering weekly, just like the pastor he counseled years earlier. Once he accepted that, he felt his faith returning. His journey back into the light began in a new and revitalized way.

The transition from two marriages into a third was not without complications. Even his daughter experienced some remorse. He and his new wife faced a lack of enthusiasm by her daughters for they were blamed for the general hurt felt by all, even ex-spouses. It was a dark time.

Everyone's reactions were understandable, and their therapist told them the normal time for such adjustments was about five years. The therapist had nailed it. They celebrated their fifth wedding anniversary with a small catered affair in his daughter's backyard. In attendance were the children of their previous marriages, including one of his former stepdaughters with her husband, son, and her son's girlfriend. The culminating moment of the event was when their children collectively gave an unrequested witness to the happiness of their marriage, and the loving acceptance of it. It was worth the five-year wait.

The reemergence of his journey brought him to a different place in his faith and in a completely different context. He called it being freed from his denominational view and released to the full expression of his faith, not limited to conventional form and function. Because of that freedom his life had changed dramatically in many ways.

His wife was undergoing hip replacement surgery, so he arrived at the hospital waiting room with plenty of reading material to occupy himself for the duration of the procedure. As he read, his mind was flooded with thoughts. It was not like those times when reading and one's mind wandered to what we ate last night or a recent football game we watched. His mind was filled with his experiences throughout the years of ministry, what they meant to him and others throughout the years. Suddenly, he had the desire to write down what he was thinking, but he had come prepared to read not write. He promptly borrowed a pen and began filling in the blank pages, margins, and any space available in the books. The words flowed with examples of his experiences and their relevance to the times of today. Before he knew it, they were calling him to join his wife in recovery. He left the hospital that day having discovered the joy of writing.

Through his most recent *dark days,* he had been filled with regret having wasted his life in ministry, studying scripture, and trying to help people through the joy of writing. He was now learning how to synthesize those experiences and leverage his learning into writing about the relevance of faith in the events of our nation today. He had come to realize that the divide between the church and state, as governed by our constitution, had been compromised, beginning with the polarization of the faith communities in politics. He learned that within the nexus of politics and faith there had been a prevailing silence of religious leaders, which led to a compromising of faith in many aspects of the faith-based politics. A further divisions in the communities along political lines had facilitated further divide in our nation.

His new understanding fueled a passion to write about these issues. A passion that allowed him to leverage his many years of experience in faith and government career. He published two works, and currently writing a third, created a blog, and routinely wrote about these issues. He reached more people in one day with his writings than he did during all the years he pastored.

Throughout this activity, his wife was his source of encouragement and inspiration. She had proved to be a valuable asset in her general wisdom and especially as his chief editor. She offered an objective view, not tainted by years of denominational faith. In addition, her skills in grammar and vocabulary far exceeded the capabilities of her engineer husband. She was the perfect compliment.

"It is not good that the man should be alone; I will make him a help meet for him." (Genesis 2:18)

He now realized that God was in this journey all along. God had never left. He was the one that had walked away. But God was never moved by our rejection or rebellion. He was in no hurry and quite content to wait.

Richard Rohr, a Franciscan priest, and notable author, described the pattern of spiritual transformation as involving three steps: Order, Disorder, and Reorder. He agreed with Rohr. Looking back, he understood the necessity of breaking down one's former habits in order to build them back with a stronger foundation. It was necessary to experience a season of disorder for God to bring a new order to his life. He now realized that this was a general principle involved in all our lives. We may not recognize God's involvement or even attribute it to anything to do with one's faith. We may refer to it as *'finding the good through the rain'* or some other phrase depicting a struggle through a difficult time only to realize a great benefit from that struggle. He believed that was just God working in all our lives, covertly and silently participating, not requiring an immediate recognition. The perfect gentleman, waiting for us to come to the end.

When darkness arrives, lean into it and persevere. Once we enter the light, we will see a new world. We must recognize that everything we have experienced was just part of the journey. We can then enjoy the rest of our life. We are in good hands.

Lynn's Thoughts ...

Such a powerful story. There is a gentleman from my spiritual past who holds my life in the palms of his hands. We have not seen each over in over fifty years, perhaps longer, but our love for each other will never die. Perhaps one day we will meet again, who knows.

A deep love between two people is not only a privilege but an honor ... a gift from the all holy. Our past can be summed up as simple as our everyday experiences. However, it seems that the younger we are, the more significant those experiences are, and unfortunately, we are usually too young to appreciate them.

Some say our paths are already designed before we are born. Others say that we create them. I'm not sure which theory is accurate, but I do know that Jerry brought back my memories. Jerry opens with returning home to a familiar soul, re-driving the well-memorized highways. But the highways of the roads or the highways of our mind? Perhaps they are the same. I have not driven my old highways in quite some time. Maybe I never will. But my soul remembers them, and those memories will last forever.

Thank you, Jerry, for the little trip down memory lane.

it WAS worth it

Onyx Rebel

"Hey, ready for court today?" Kathy asked. "He's here with his lawyer."

I sat next to her, handing over the coffee I had bought for her this morning. I couldn't sleep last night so I was ready early.

"Oh God," she said. "Thank you so much. I didn't have a chance to have any yet. Did you read over everything? Any questions?"

"Yeah, but why do I have to answer more questions? I didn't agree to anything yet." I shrugged and lowered my eyes.

She patted my shoulder. "You've done nothing wrong. I just want you to be prepared. He's an asshole, but the judge doesn't know that yet. If he shoots off at the mouth like he did with the last one, he'll see right through him." Kathy smiled.

"I'm just tired of coming here and feeling like nothing is working."

I'd been to court three times for a restraining order. But a court advocate convinced me to drop my complaint because emotional abuse was hard to prove. Sat here another two times for child support and now for the divorce.

"There's been progress," Kathy said. "We have his financials now. And that was the last holdup. Let's see what happens today. They've already had their continuance, so they can't ask for another." She glanced at her watch and stood.

I followed her into the courtroom and took a seat in the back, resenting that I had a favorite spot. I made sure not to look in his direction. His lawyer stood and stepped over to my lawyer. They walked through the double doors, and I watched as they closed behind them. My phone vibrated. It was Kathy asking if I had the receipts for the truck repair. The truck we bought together – the truck I was driving – until he had it towed from my apartment. He just wanted to snoop. Find information he could use against me. The thing was taken like a thief in middle of the night. In a way, it helped with my anxiety once it was gone. I no longer worried he was outside my window. And ... he couldn't threaten to take the truck if I didn't have it. I finally bought a car, and he couldn't take that.

I searched my emails and bank statements until I found what she wanted. I texted it to her and waited. I received a reply.

Courtroom D2 was strictly for divorces. Two smaller rooms on either side of the entry were for lawyers and their clients. I entered and sat in the room on the right. Kathy shuffled some papers and smiled at me.

"His lawyer is talking to him now," she said.

I tilted my head.

"Settlement," she added. "Things are not in his favor. I've been looking over the financials, and I'm asking for $140,000 just for your portion of the house."

I was speechless. He had told me over and over again I would never get more than twenty thousand from him. He said I didn't deserve anything more. I would have nothing if it wasn't for him. My first lawyer encouraged me to accept the $20,000 he had offered and be done with it all. I stared at Kathy and frowned.

She tilted her head and nodded.

"Okay, but how does this all work?"

"I'll let his lawyer know that you agree with the amount," she said. "Wait here."

Kathy didn't return. My back ached, and I had to use the lady's room.

"She doesn't deserve shit! How can you let her take my money? I'm paying you to keep that bitch away from it!" my ex's voice boomed through the short hallway.

"Mr. Hillard ... please calm down," a man's voice stated. "Let's go back to the room and talk about this in private." His lawyer gave me an odd look as he pushed my ex away from me.

My heart pounded and my head spun. *Here we go again.* I almost ran back to the small room, praying to find my lawyer. "Are you okay?" I asked Kathy, my bathroom needs forgotten. "I heard him yelling."

"All's good," she replied with a wink. "He just realizes he's not gonna win and is acting like the child he is. I think he was eavesdropping at the door when I was talking to his lawyer. He burst in and started calling us names."

The room whirled and I had to sit. I was used to him calling me names, but to yell at my lawyer? I figured he'd act a little more professional. "I'm so sorry. He gets like that when he's upset."

"Stop apologizing for the man," Kathy stated. "I understand what you went through and I'm sorry. But it's almost over. His lawyer knows his client must settle before court."

We left the small room, and I stood in the hallway. My ex and his lawyer were about twenty feet away. Kathy walked over and nodded. She handed him a slip of paper. His lawyer turned and whispered to my ex who shook his head. For over three hours, the three bantered and nodded and bantered and yelled and bantered and nodded. Just before dark, everyone agreed on a final number.

The stress I faced in that little room I never wanted to experience again. The minute details. The repercussions. The deadlines. Legal jargon I barely understood. When it was all over and notarized, I felt mentally and emotionally drained. I was hungry and tired and wanted to go home. Instead, I visited the lady's room so I wouldn't run into him in the parking lot.

Standing by my car under the moonlight, Kathy waved at me.

I walked over and smiled. "I really appreciate you fighting for me and taking the case when I didn't have the funds. I don't know what I would've done without you."

"I'm happy I was able to help. Take some time for yourself. We'll get together some day and celebrate."

I nodded. "Of course."

As I drove home, I thought of all the pain I endured. I thought of all the times he made me feel like I wasn't doing enough as a wife. I remembered how weak he made me feel. How he would threaten if I tried to leave. The threats started with how I ruined his life. Eventually, they expanded to our daughter, and how he should have her and not me. Because his earnings were higher, I wouldn't be able to properly care for her financially. He often hid my car keys so I couldn't leave. He drained money from our joint accounts. He talked shit about me to his parent and my family, which started arguments. He told me that my sister and friends were jealous, and the attention I gave them I should be giving to him instead. How I didn't love him enough. I did not want to have sex with him, and he would yell that it was my obligation. In God's eyes, according to him, we were one and it was my duty. I was depressed and tired all the time, believing if I just tried harder ...

It wasn't until I graduated with my CNA certificate that I slowly gained confidence in myself. When I earned my associates degree, I moved from that isolated town to where I had friends and family. That was when I realized my divorce was not my fault. I was not the crazy one. I had just been gaslighted.

Others started seeing the real him. When we were living as man and wife, he acted loving and caring while around others. But when we were alone ...

When I enrolled for my bachelor's degree, I knew I would be okay. Once I had that degree, he wouldn't be able to say I couldn't take care of our daughter anymore. I sometimes look back on the pain and accept that I caused more by not leaving earlier. I was afraid of losing out on family events because if we ever arrived at the same time, we would fight.

"Mommy, you're back!" My daughter gave me a hug.

Inside my heart, I could never regret the nine years I spent with him. Because without him, I would not have her. She gave meaning to my life, and I will forever be grateful.

"Hey, munchkin. What do you think about us moving to a bigger place?" I asked.

"With a backyard? And a puppy?"

I could not help but laugh. "Yes, with a backyard, and we'll talk about the puppy later."

Lynn's Thoughts …

What I don't understand is this … we fall in love with the perfect man. Sometimes, we even have children with him. Then everything falls apart and suddenly the boxing gloves go on. How can we love someone so much only to turn around and hate them the next day?

I was told once that love was nothing more than a chemical reaction. A chemical reaction? Okay, does that mean there's an antidote to falling for someone?

Onyx's depiction of this woman's ability to drag herself back from the pits is excellent. A must read for every young woman. A wonderful relationship is a blessing, but when it turns sour, there is nothing more bitter.

If only … our lives are filled with *if onlys*. If only I had …

How do we live to avoid our *if onlys?* Can we avoid them?

I don't think so, because then we would not be who we are today. As I always say, "Don't get mad, get stronger."

Knitting in the Dark

Morna Gersho

"HONEY, I GOT good news and bad news," my husband stated. "Which do you want first?"

I picked the bad, because that was how I rolled.

"I broke your grandmother's depression glass butter dish."

I gasped.

"But your mom's friend, Nancy, wants you to call her." He had inserted his good news and waited.

I couldn't believe it. My head spun and my heart raced. Would I finally meet someone who was close to my mom? Someone who actually knew her? Someone who could help me connect the dots?

My mother fell sick when I was little. We called it, 'The accident.' I don't know why we called it that. It wasn't a real accident. There was nothing accidental about it. Looking back, I think that was how we made it neat and tidy. Just another way to help us cope with a traumatic event of epic proportion. It maimed us and stayed with us.

Because my mom fell ill when I was young, my father moved us away from everyone we knew, and most importantly, from my mother. We ended up on the west coast. A big mistake, but a change purely for survival. He carefully packed every part of her away – pictures, clothing – anything that would remind us of our mother. We were not to think or speak about her. We were pushed into virtual silence. If one of us cried, the others would offer to support but also caution, "If you start crying, it'll make us all cry." We pretended to be strong, act as if my mother's accident wasn't traumatic. It was just the way my father chose to handle his grief – and that made it exponentially worse for us kids. Instead of only once, we lost our mother multiple times.

The first few calls to my mother's friend built a sense of familiarity. Nancy lived on the east coast just an hour from my relatives in New Jersey. I set up a trip, and while my family visited the Bronx Zoo, I visited Nancy in Yonkers, New York. Our first meeting was full of trepidation. I even set up a pretense for my husband to call from the zoo to provide me a quick *exit*. But it wasn't needed.

The threads were soon sewn. Nancy and I were like old blankets. We felt warm and familiar. As it turned out, there wasn't enough time that afternoon for us to cover everything. When my husband arrived with our daughter, I couldn't begin to account for the time. A ritual for our future visits. As we pulled away, I smiled and waved. Something inside me had changed. I couldn't describe it, but it felt good and safe.

The funny thing was that what had started as just a random afternoon grew into so much more. It grew into twenty years of east coast visits – each richer than the last. Three and four-day weekends full of sleeping in, delectable meals, and non-stop talking.

The visits began innocently at first. Inevitably, they ended with us planning the next. We rarely left Nancy's kitchen, but within our minds, we were traveling. Not geographically, but through time. With each story, I was able to explore my mom's personality. Like a character flushed from an artist's sketchbook, my mother became a three-dimensional person.

Nancy and my mother were more than just friends. They also enjoyed compatible academic careers. My mother studied piano while in college and Nancy studied voice. They accompanied each other during their performances. Nancy not only had anecdotes to share, but she had a few dogeared concert programs, annotated with my mother's beautiful script. My mother had narrated highlights of each concert in the margins, and her humor shone through the ink with critiques of performers' fashion and makeup mistakes.

We would talk into the wee hours of the morning until we were bleary eyed and our throats dry. I was so desperate in the beginning, I once followed Nancy to the bathroom. I stood outside the door with the glass doorknob and impatiently waited. I just didn't want our conversations to stop. I drank up every word.

I never met anyone who had personally witnessed the horrible tragedy, but who was also a participant. I knew there were doctors and such, but her old friends were scarce. My aunt was technically a first cousin, but I often wondered if her allegiance was more of a sense of familial obligation. I never met anyone who actually knew everyone in my family. But Nancy knew my grandparents on both sides. She knew my aunts and uncles.

My mother had her accident in the late sixties, and I met Nancy in the nineties. Anyone privy to my mother's traumatic event had simply disappeared. By the time I was old enough to reach out, not many were alive or cognitively intact.

Through the years, I built my mom inside my mind from scratch. Although it was painful, the joy was more powerful. The exhilaration of learning something about my mother overshadowed the pain. The pain that did hit was from the realization of what I had lost. What had been stolen from me.

The more I learned about her, the more real she became. There was, however, some things I didn't want to know. And for just a moment, I wondered if I'd be better off not knowing.

Eventually, others came forward to share their stories about my mother. My father even gave me her calendars. Three years of complimentary gas station calendars with each square crammed with activities, recorded in her perfect script, belaying her effortless perfection.

Another of my mother's first cousin once revealed, "She could knit in the dark at the movies!"

I couldn't crochet in the light.

A friend down the street from my grandparents said that my mother once scooped up my three-year-old sister in the midst of a tantrum and left without a single word. "Your mother was wearing an A-line, white sheath. A mother of four wearing white?" the lady said. "Your mother gave me hope."

When my mother first became ill, she lived with my grandparents, and was later moved to a home. A blood clot caused her to collapse, and no one knew CPR. She was without oxygen for over six minutes. Because of the brain damage, the doctors could not bring her back, not fully. She had to relearn everything, including her children's names, who she was, basic math, and anything else we could imagine. Her psychological evaluations placed her aptitude at that of a twelve-year-old.

I shared my mother's story many times, and the reaction was always the same. 'The loss of a parent is terrible.' But losing her twice was akin to tossing gasoline on a fire.

As I grew older, I visited her in North Carolina. Dealing with someone with brain damage was difficult. It required patience and consistency. I loved my mother. There was nothing I wouldn't have done for her, but the explaining and constant repeating myself felt exasperating. Many times, I cried in the parking lot after leaving her. Sometimes, I would step outside and count to ten before re-entering her room because she was upset over a missing item. The item had been missing for years or may not have ever existed. I would patiently redirect her.

Somehow, the contact with Nancy sandwiched between visits with my mother gradually changed things inside me. The random sharing moved my world from black and white to full color. I was becoming more patient or perhaps more tolerant.

One afternoon, I stood outside a department store's dressing room, tapping my foot. My mom refused to move. But, I wasn't angry.

"My shoes have to match my purse!" my mom called out.

I took in a deep breath and laughed silently. "Just come out ... we'll find the purse later."

"No!" she stated. "They have to match!"

Thanks to Nancy's stories, I remained calm. My mother's confusion had nothing to do with her brain damage. It was her keen sense of fashion, and the crazy misplaced allegiance to etiquette from Raleigh in the late forties.

The salesperson popped her head in the entryway.

"Any chance you could look for a small, white clutch as an accessory?" I whispered.

She nodded.

Nancy laughed so hard when I shared that story. "You have to understand that we were not allowed in town without our gloves and a hat. And ... our purses had to match our shoes." She shook her head. "Wouldn't be caught dead with mismatched accessories."

I laughed, remembering. Nancy had taught me well.

Nancy had given my mother back to me. We may have lost her in sixty-six, but she was slowly returning to me. I now admired and was proud of her. I saw the similarities between her and me. I wore a new badge of honor. Even though I was only three when my mother became ill, she left her mark. She was there all along.

My mother handled my children so deftly that they never knew what hit them. Playing absentmindedly, they refused to come downstairs to say good-bye. I was upset.

"If the mountain won't come to Mohammad," my mother stated, "then Mohammad must come to the mountain."

She slowly climbed my aunt's worn, walnut stairs. The door creaked open, and my children peered up with wide eyes. They ran and hugged her legs. I stood silently in awe. I could have threatened, but still not received the same results.

On a flight home, I thought about my mom. For the first time, I could see her as a whole person – as complete. I no longer felt that searing, burning pain of loss. Something had changed in me. I could now stand back, watch, and enjoy. I could love her for who she was today and not what she was yesterday. Her humor, her savviness, her efficiency, her intelligence, and ability to make everything look easy gave me hope.

My mother was perfect for she could knit in the dark.

Lynn's Thoughts …

Nothing is worse than losing a parent. I remember when my mother passed, I asked my cousin everything I could about her. I couldn't seem to ask the questions fast enough.

Morna gives a close and personal description of what it is like searching for a parent. And what is sometimes difficult for us to understand is that our parents were young once too. As we age, we change. We tend to calm down and react to things differently. What adult children do not see in their aging parents are young teens, those with high hopes and large dreams.

But Morna sees it, she sees it all.

Brain damage is nothing to cheer about, but if we can look past the silly little actions, maybe we can find that person in there somewhere. Life has a way of churning up everything to where the colors blend, the yellows are no longer bright, the whites are dull, and the blues are more purple. The shadows tend to darken and the creases tend to deepen.

But if you take the time, maybe you too will find the perfection, just like Morna did, for knitting in the dark is an extraordinary talent.

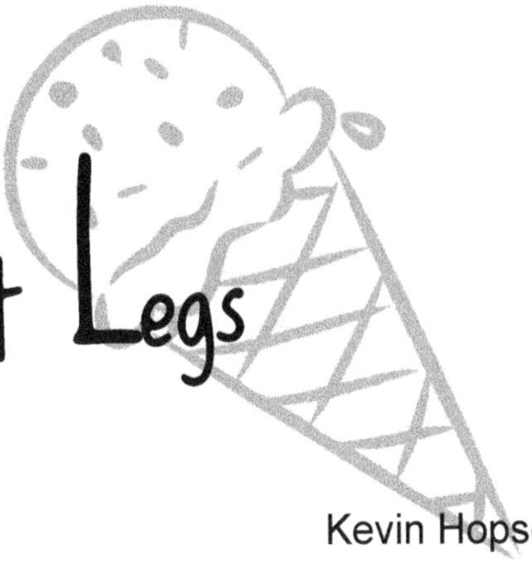

Last Legs

Kevin Hopson

I'd been on my feet for almost eight hours, and thankfully, my shift at the coffee shop was nearing an end. It was a weekday, and the lunch crowd had peaked a couple of hours ago. It was the middle of an afternoon lull.

I was about to relax when the door opened, and a young boy stepped inside. He looked to be about eleven or twelve, a mop of brown hair covering his head. He sat at a nearby table. As I approached, his hazel eyes met my gaze.

"Hello, sir," he said.

I glimpsed at the entrance half expecting to see his family. But no one followed. "Hi … is it just you?"

The boy nodded. "Can I get a glass of water, please? It's free, right?"

"Only if it's water from the tap. Bottled water costs three dollars."

"Tap water is fine," he replied. "Do you have a menu?"

Despite being a coffee shop, we also sold ice cream. It tended to be more popular than our coffee.

"There's a menu on the big chalkboard behind the counter." I pointed. "You order at the counter."

The boy squinted at the chalkboard, then turned his attention back to me. "But you can take my order, right?"

I sighed and forced a smile. "I suppose. What would you like?"

"I don't know. Never been here before."

I wasn't sure what the kid wanted. Recite the entire menu to him? He obviously wasn't making an attempt to read the chalkboard.

"I'm guessing you want ice cream?" I asked.

"Oh, yeah. Definitely."

"We have sundaes, cones, and bowls."

"How much does a sundae cost?"

I sighed. "Depends on the type. They range from three to five dollars."

The boy mulled it over. "I probably don't have enough for a sundae. How about cones?"

"Cones and bowls cost the same. Unless you want a waffle cone. That's fifty cents extra. The cost varies, though, based on how many scoops you want."

"Okay." He pursed his lips for a moment. "How much for a single scoop?"

"Two dollars."

The kid furrowed his brows.

I swallowed, choking down my frustration. Don't get me wrong. I like kids. It's just that this particular one was wearing on me.

"Is there anything cheaper?" he asked.

I huffed. "We have a junior bowl for a dollar and twenty-five cents. It's basically a single scoop for kids."

The boy bobbed his head. "That sounds good. Do you have mint chocolate chip?"

"We sure do." I'd never been so relieved to have mint chocolate chip in the shop. "Will that be it?"

"Yeah. That and the water."

"Sure." I wrote down the order and tore the sheet from my pad. "It will be one dollar and thirty-five cents."

"I pay now?"

"That's how it usually works."

"Okay. No problem."

He pulled a couple of dollars from his pocket and handed them to me.

"Great. I'll be back with your order along with your change."

I walked toward the counter, my calves tight, and my feet aching. I made my way behind the cash register. One end of the counter housed coffee products, while the other displayed a dozen flavors of ice cream. After gathering the change, I grabbed a glass and filled it with tap water.

"I need a junior bowl with mint chocolate chip," I said to my co-worker.

"You got it," she replied.

I circled around the counter and waited. A few seconds later, she reached across with a small cup in hand.

"Thanks," I said.

"No problem."

I returned to the boy's table, placing the ice cream and water in front of him.

"Thanks," he said.

"You're welcome, and here's your change." I placed the coins into the boy's cupped hand. "If you need anything else, let me know."

"I will. Thanks again."

I only had ten minutes left in my shift, but I couldn't bear it any longer. I plopped down in a chair at another table, watching the kid enjoy his ice cream while my feet thanked me for the break.

The boy stood to leave a few minutes later, and that's when I noticed something on the table. As tired as I was, I jumped to my feet, my eyes bulging at the sight.

"Wait!" I shouted.

He was nearly at the door when he spun around.

"You left money behind," I said.

"I know. It's your tip."

It was a five-dollar bill.

"But you said you didn't have enough money for a sundae."

"I didn't," he said. "Not when I was planning to leave a five-dollar tip. That's my weekly allowance, but I figured you needed it more than me."

I was at a loss for words. "Thanks." It was all I could say.

"You're welcome," he said with a small smile.

My lips stretched into a grin, and I waved as he left. I guess it paid to be nice to people. In more ways than one.

Lynn's Thoughts …

This story gives me hope. Perhaps the upcoming generations have a little insight into life after all.

Although the story is short, the separation of the ages is long and deep. A little guy helping an older guy. I love it.

Many times we judge others by how tired we are … or how our day is treating us. The strengths of another are often hidden, and unless we're willing to wait, we just might miss them.

A little one wants a little ice cream but is willing to do with less to give more to another. Why can't we do this all the time – pass a little kindness to another? Maybe if everyone was willing to do with a little less the world would be in much better shape.

On only a few pages, Kevin has weaved a world of wonder through frozen cream and a five-dollar bill. But what was hidden under the napkins and trash was a lot more … it was hope for a brighter future.

Mama Luisa

Thomas Bell

Matrimonio del Secuestro - Spanish (Mexico) for marriage by kidnapping. Thought to be rooted in the Moorish traditions of the Spanish but also a common practice of the pre-colonial tribes of the Mexican Republic.

The boy's hand slid down the back of her dress, his small fingers resting on her bottom. The Banda music blared, and a barely perceptible grin spread across his face. He rested his chin on her shoulder as her heavy bosom brushed against his chest, they moved in unison.

A whistle blew from the packed tables where men drank in the dark, hunkered down under smokey clouds, far away from the dimly lit candles. The whistle was for the boy, for the improprieties of his fingers. He knew they were only concerned that he had the guts to do what they wanted to do. The girl was a gift. A gift he intended to enjoy. He dropped his hand lower, touching more and praying the song would never end.

The light shifted in the doorway, and a bulky outline filled the cave-like entrance before disappearing inside the crowd – skirts swooshed, blue-black braids bounced, sandaled feet lost amongst huaraches, boots, and cheap leather dress shoes.

The ballad ended, and the girl gave a playful push against the boy. Her chest heaved, and the boy's cheeks darkened. The dance had been slow.

"¿Cómo te llamas?" he asked.

She moved her lips, and he tilted his felt sombrero, bringing his ear closer.

"Renalta," she repeated.

"Mucho gusto." He placed a hand over his heart but was cut off by a heartfelt grito and subsequent clang of the band starting up again. He pulled off his sombrero, brushed back his long, black hair, and pointed at the doorway. The night air would be cooler and quieter. Perhaps he could tell her his name.

She nodded.

They made their way to the doorway, and the whistle blew again. He winced. The night air felt cool, and the silence was deafening after listening to the blaring music. The moon cast a bluish-gray shadow across Renalta's face. Her beauty was almost lost saved for certain accents – the tip of her delicate nose, her rounded chin offsetting her slender neck. He resisted the urge to hold her.

A group of men, bundled in serapes, stood off from the doorway, passing around a bottle of mezcal and puffing vigorously on tobacco. The boy eyed them, taking the girl's hand and gently pulling her deeper into the night.

"You like Banda?" he asked.

"The snare really moves the music. And it's loud."

He glanced at her. A small bead of sweat clung to the side of her face. He reached up and softly dabbed it away. He hesitated before caressing her cheek. Her mouth, slightly open, tugged at his eyes.

"It is loud, isn't it?" He leaned in and his lips found hers. His sombrero pushed back by the force of her forehead.

A voice drew his attention to the door behind the girl.

"Suave, abuela. Let the kids have their fun."

The silhouette of a large-bosomed Indian woman stepped closer to the lingering men. She could've been thirty or eighty, there was no way of telling inside the enduring shadows. Her traditional skirts covered her busty chest and large backside and ended at two ankles that couldn't possibly hold such a body. Her intricately embroidered vest, even in the faint moonlight, was alive with color. Her face had the lines of someone who toiled the land, crimson circles decorated her cheeks from hours of sun and wind. She wore no rebozo like most women.

Just like Renalta.

"Renalta, hijita! What are you doing over there?"

"Coming, mama!" Renalta smiled at him. "That's my mother."

They made plans to meet in the morning, and he squeezed her hand. He watched her fade into the darkness. Renalta never look back, but he was still grinning.

He had kissed her! There was only one thing to do when he was feeling this good – get drunk.

He jumped as water soaked the clothes he still wore from the night before. "Hijo de puta –"

Renalta's mother stared down at him.

"Was that necessary, senõra?"

"I've been trying to wake you for the last five minutes." Her voice held that distinct twang from the tribes of the upper Sierra Madres, her words clipped and her cadence flat.

"A thousand pardons, senõra. I've been looking forward to our meeting this morning –"

"I had a hell of a time finding you. She never told me your name."

"I'm Memo, senõra." He swayed on his feet, trying to look dignified, but still too drunk to wonder why this woman stood in his room at the boarding house with a now empty bucket.

"She is missing."

He smiled – his mind searching for the meaning. "Who is missing, senõra?"

"My Renalta." Her hands balled into fists at her sides.

Memo glanced down at her ankles and frowned. How could they hold up such a powerful body? "What?"

A small group of nosy onlookers gathered behind her. She glanced over her shoulder before adding, "Come outside." She pushed her way through the riff-raff.

"Let me grab my hat." Despite his sombrero, Memo winced at the bright light of the street. "I know this town, senõra. I'll help find her."

Mama Luisa glared deeply into his eyes. The hair above her mouth slowly curved into a frown. "Those men took her."

"What men?"

She reached up and pointed her worn finger at his chest. The sleeve of her shirt rolled back revealing an ashy arm. "You're going to help me find her."

"Have you been to the comisaria?"

"Of course. Those pendejos either know something or are too lazy to help. I've already wasted time finding you. Do you know who those men are that spoke to me last night outside the salon?"

Memo shook his head. "Let me think …" He rubbed his throbbing forehead. He'd been looking forward to coffee with … "Regio? A real drunk. Wait … you never said she was missing."

"We're staying in the pension behind town hall. There was a commotion last night. When I went to look, the side gate was open and – "

"And you think Regio …"

"I don't think anything. But I didn't like their attitude."

"Esta bien. Let's start there. I know his house is on the east side past the irrigation ditch."

"Take me there."

The two stood in front of a small adobe shaded by an old huisache tree. A pack of dogs eyed them from down the street before disappearing behind a fence. Nearby children, however, didn't give up so easily. They stared with blank faces and bare feet.

Memo smiled and tipped his hat.

"What's taking so long?" Luisa frowned, clenching her fists.

"It's early for him."

"This would go faster if we had something to ride."

"I have much to offer, senõra Luisa, but not a horse."

She looked at him, flexed her fingers, allowing them to hang at her sides. Her downturned mouth eased slightly. "I was speaking about a burro."

Memo chuckled. "Of course, senõra."

The door opened. A man with disheveled hair glared at them. "¿Que pasa aquí? Mamá? Are you still hounding Memo? Give him a break, will yah?"

Memo shook his head. "Buenos días, Regio –"

"Regio, my daughter's missing. Something bad will happen to her …" Her voice faltered and she paused. "Can you help or not?"

"Missing?" Regio scowled. "And that brought you here … to me?"

Memo started to interject, ease the tension, but a young girl ran up, making him jump. "¡Hijole!"

Regio stepped out of the doorway. "Get outta here, you rat!" He waved at the young child.

"Leave the girl alone!" Luisa yelled. She placed her hand on the girl's shoulder, but the girl kept her eyes on Memo.

"She won't stop following us." Memo waved at the barefoot street urchin but she continued to follow, staring at him.

"Oh, leave her be," Luisa said. "Can you take me to the place Regio mentioned?"

Memo pushed his sombrero back on his head and rubbed his eyes. He felt sick and wanted coffee but couldn't bring himself to ask her to wait.

"Listen, senõra, even if Regio's right, we can't just go into a place like that. These aren't the type you can scold. Where's your husband?"

"Drunk. And I wasn't planning on talking my way out of this. I'll use this if I have to." She pulled out a sawed-off shotgun before hiding it back under her skirt.

"¡Chingada madre! Luisa … this is getting to be a little much. I don't even know you. I'm not sure I can –"

"Just take me there. I'll get my daughter back by myself."

Memo thought about Renalta and the kiss. His heart pounded and he studied Luisa, standing in the street, her braids frayed, her face sun worn. He couldn't imagine how her beautiful daughter would someday resemble her. "Oh hell. I can't let you go in there alone. We're gonna need to borrow two burros. It's about a day's ride. And we'll need another weapon. Let me talk to some friends. I'll meet you in the plaza in an hour."

"Gracias, mi hijo." Luisa gave him a sad smile before touching his arm.

"Oh, and Luisa, get us some food?"

"Give me the gun, Chuncho."

"No!" Chuncho remained on the cot at the boarding house, shirtless and smoking a cigarette with supreme insolence. Thick hair bunched on top of his head like a helmet. "And keep your voice down or they'll kick me out."

"Why not?" Memo's voice raised. "Why not?"

"Look at you. You're all worked up." Chuncho took a drag and spoke from behind a wall of smoke. "The state you're in, you'll probably end up getting yourself killed, and I'll end up with nothing."

"I'll leave you something in return."

Chuncho let out a hearty laugh. "But you have nothing now!"

It was true. Memo had nothing to barter with. "My sombrero? It's felt."

"That old thing?"

"Chuncho, I'm sorry but I need that weapon. I'll just take it if I have to."

"You're funny." Chuncho scratched his belly and rolled onto his side.

"I'm sorry." Memo stepped closer and popped him in the nose.

Chuncho's eyes widened and watered. "What the fu –"

Memo punched him again on the side of the head.

"Ow!" Chuncho dropped the cigarette and hid behind his hands. His exposed brown belly had just become a tempting target. Memo stepped back and gave it his all. His right hand dug deep and

Chuncho wasn't ready for it. He let out a long, sad exhale, his face hanging off the side of the cot. He gasped for air.

"I'm sorry, amigo." Memo pulled various things from under the cot until he found an old folded up poncho. Inside was a long-barreled Navy Colt with little flecks of rust on the trigger guard. The wood inlay of the handle browning with age. Memo checked to see that it was loaded before shoving it into his pants. He pulled his jacket closed around his waist and stepped to the doorway. "I'll do anything for you, old pal."

"You asshole. I hope you get yourself killed."

"You don't mean it."

"Like hell I don't."

"Where'd you get the burros, mi hijo?"

They were riding into the hills. The sun was setting, and a string of clouds clung to the distant peaks.

"I told you, senõra, that I couldn't offer a horse. I work for a man that rents burros to local farmers."

"He let you borrow these?" Mama Luisa's voice had lost some of its harsh tones. Maybe the burros helped her feel they were getting somewhere.

Memo jolted along with the small, sure-footed animal. He grinned. "Of course, senõra."

It was still dark when they arrived at the canyon.

"I've only been through here once," Memo said. "The place Regio mentioned is next to the creek. Down there." He pointed. "We'll leave the animals here. They might choose the wrong time to start braying."

As he tied together the burros, Mama Luisa prayed on her knees. She made the sign of the cross in a way Memo had never seen. He made his own sign. They walked down the dark trail, and the distant sounds from the creek grew louder. The ground leveled, and the silhouette of a small, jacal, a thatched wattle and daub hut, was nestled between two Rosewood trees. The fading moonlight still reflecting off the tin roof.

Mama Luisa was about to charge in, but Memo held onto her shoulder.

"Be careful with that thing." He nodded at the shotgun in her hands. "It's likely to spray more than you think."

She glanced over her shoulder and replied, "You think I haven't used this before?"

They stopped at the door and listened. Memo stepped around the side of the small hut and held up his fingers, confirming that there were two horses in the makeshift corral.

Mama Luisa nodded, and without a second's thought, kicked the door open.

¡Dios mio! Was there anything those ankles couldn't do? Memo's eyes had adjusted to the dark outside, but inside the hut with no light, he strained to see. Luisa had already moved to a darker corner and was kneeling beside a shadowed bundle.

A half-asleep voice echoed out from across the room. "¿Que chingados es este?"

The room lit in a burst of light as flames blasted from the barrel of Luisa's shotgun. Memo stood frozen in the doorway, gun at his side. Luisa pushed past cradling Renalta under her arm.

A shrill whistle echoed out from the darkness followed by a voice.

"Hey, lover boy! What did that bitch just do?"

Memo aimed at the voice and fired six times … boom, boom, boom, boom, boom, boom. He waited for return fire, but none came. His ears rang in the silence.

The whinny of horses brought Memo from his trance. "Luisa! Someone's coming."

Luisa sat on the ground with her daughter in her lap like a young child, stroking her hair and whispering in her ear.

"Luisa! We need to go. They'll hang you for this!"

"Hang me? After what they've done to my baby?"

"Yes."

She continued to stroke Renalta's hair. The embroidery of her vest glimmered in the moonlight like the night he first met her.

"Take the horses! Go back to your people. Go now! There's not much time. I'll prepare the saddles."

He helped Luisa onto the horse's back. The feel of Renalta's dress brought him back to the night they danced and kissed. Her hair was now a mess and her face bruised.

"Take care of yourself, Renalta," he said, helping her up. "It was a pleasure to dance with you."

In the yard behind the municipality, not far from where Mama Luisa and Renalta had stayed two nights prior, Memo stood on a bench under the oak tree. He tilted his head and brought his shoulder up and itched where the hemp rope was irritating his neck. A small crowd had gathered – church had ended. Chuncho was there, wearing a shirt for once, and Memo's sombrero. But he refused to meet Memo's eye. And where was Regio? Probably too hungover.

A uniformed Rurale stepped up. No announcement or final words. Memo couldn't afford it. He found himself thinking about Mama Luisa's ankles. They were really something.

His eyes scanned the crowd one last time. In the very back, he spotted the face of the little street urchin. How did she get in?

Memo smiled.

The little girl smiled back.

Lynn's Thoughts …

Selling and stealing of women, not an old concept. Something that has been around as long as the human population has breathed.

Thomas gives us a horror ride into the land of kidnapping and sex-trading. He also worded his lines in a way that made you feel as if you were actually in another country. However, one message was loud and clear. People are the same everywhere.

A mother will fight for her child, and a good friend will risk their life for the same, no matter the country or the hemisphere. We all have fears and hopes, and we all love and hate. The only difference may be the food we eat or the homes we live in. We all work. We all care for our families. And we all have at least one uncle who drinks too much.

And no matter where you were born on this crazy planet of ours, someone will come for you when you are ready. How odd it is that we all think the same.

Rainy Day Memories

Roger Guffey

My earliest memory of rain dates back to the birth of my youngest brother. It was a gray November day when my father turned his blue Chrysler Imperial onto the lane of my maternal grandparents' homeplace where we stayed until Jack was born. The slow drizzle peppered the ground, filling the air with that marvelous aroma of rain falling onto thirsty dust.

Memories can be transient for most, but researchers have documented six people blessed (or cursed) with perfect memories. These remarkable individuals can recall not only events, but the weather and other newsworthy stories. I can remember some days clearly because it rained on those days. Raindrops falling on the tin roof of our smokehouse sang a hymn that lulled me to a pleasant slumber. On many a rainy day, I would curl up on the cheesecloths my father used to protect the hams hanging from the rafters as they cured. The houses of my maternal grandmother, Maggie, and my Aunt Ruby also had tin roofs that murmured softly during slow rains. When the rain was heavy, that murmur became a pounding roar that was so loud I could not sleep.

Although our house sat on a hill that prevented it from flooding, rains would wash away the loose gravel, and Dad expected his sons to carry it back up. The heaviest rainstorms would fill the ditches with knee-deep water where we could splash and play. One year, I gave a chicken duck eggs to incubate. When I took the ducklings to swim in the ditch, the terrified mother hen ran around frantically, clucking to lure them out of the water.

Unless a rainstorm was accompanied by lightning, I reveled in the drizzle, frequently sneaking to the woodlands where the rain hitting the leaves offered a sense of happiness. Sometimes, I built a crude lean-to where I took shelter and imagined I was a pioneer hiding from Indians.

Some memories were downright macabre. For several years, the hogs we raised to fund my college were allowed to roam freely over our small farm. Our chickens followed them to catch the insects they flushed from the grass. On a rainy day, one of our sows devoured a hen, developing a taste for poultry. The never-ending traffic of pigs' feet had killed the vegetation near the barn, and on rainy days, it became one large mudhole. The foolish chickens that wandered into this quagmire became trapped. For the predatory sow, this was a smorgasbord, and she soon learned to take advantage of the chickens' plight.

Like many residents of Appalachia, my most treasured riches were the simple things in our everyday lives. My brother, Leonard, took Jack and me to a neighbor's ponds to fish on the same day my mom hosted a bridal shower for him and his fiancée. A light rain pelted the surface of the water, causing hundreds of small, ever-widening circles. The pond teemed with scores of catfish that eagerly attacked our earthworm baits. In just a few minutes, we had caught over sixty that we carried home in a fifty-pound lard stand. We emptied them into a stock-watering barrel where they lived for several months.

One memory that I relive fondly was the day I was helping my father build a new smokehouse and raindrops fell. I had started to the house when Dad asked me where I was headed. I replied, "It's raining so I figured we'd quit."

Without missing a beat, he reassured me, "Don't worry. Shit'll float." I never complained about being in the rain again.

In July before my dad died that November, my youngest brother and I decided to visit where Dad was born on top of Edwards Mountain. Robert Harmon, one of Dad's lifelong friends, agreed to take us to the abandoned homeplace. The mountainside was steep so we had to take our time to reach the top. Along the way, we passed chestnut stumps standing like tall tombstones, marking their last desperate efforts to survive the insidious chestnut blight that had reduced their number from two billion to almost none. Pioneers would harvest chestnuts in the fall and use the tannin-rich wood that resisted decay to build split-rail and picket fencing. Young trees often sprouted from the still-living roots, but the latent spores killed them before they produced chestnuts.

An abandoned logging road ran across the top of the mountain to the clearing where my dad's homeplace once stood. Only two logs from the original house were still there, but orange daylilies grew in abundance in the dappled sunlight. A sandstone rock marked where the front door of the blacksmith shop had been. During our trek, a massive thunderstorm had rolled in bringing a gully-buster that drove us back to the truck.

One memory of rain indelibly etched into my brain involved my oldest sister, Sally. I had four brothers and two sisters, but Sally and I were always close. She gave me my middle name and often rocked me to sleep to the strains of *Barbara Allen.* I was a victim of a hit-and-run in my junior year in college and had to be resuscitated in the ICU. Sally was the first face I saw when I woke. She said, "Welcome home, feller."

Sally was sixteen years older than me and was married by the time I turned six. She often accompanied me when I roamed the hills and hollers taking photographs. On one such trip, she asked me to take her to her husband's grandfather's homeplace on Raleigh Creek – the other side of Spann Hill. A spring rain threatened us, but we pushed on to a gravel road so steep that my car refused to climb back to the top. Sally stepped out and pushed the car to get it going again. We enjoyed recounting our little adventure to our family who thought we were lucky to get out at all.

The most treasured memory I have of Sally is the afternoon we spent picking blackberries on the far side of Turkey Ridge where my parents lived. Blackberries grew abundantly in those pastures so we optimistically always carried four buckets. A rainstorm sprang up just as we had filled them, and a light drizzle began to fall. There was no lightning so we strolled home slowly, reminiscing about misadventures of our youth, enjoying the heaven-sent baptism as an affirmation of the simple pleasures that blessed beyond measure.

The memory of that rainy walk is as fresh in my mind today as it was fifty years ago, but life moved on. Our parents died twenty years ago and my younger brother, who inherited the homeplace, turned the barn into a cabinet shop. The tin-roofed smokehouse where I used to nap on rainy days was torn down. By far the worst change was the diagnosis that Sally had developed Parkinson's disease. It rapidly debilitated her frail body with tremors and an unsteady gait. Gone was the sixteen-year-old who straddled the ridge row of the house to paint the gable for money to buy a prom dress. The woman who calmly told her husband that he just plowed two copperheads out of the potato row. Her face that once beamed with life, love, and laughter now displayed the flat affect caused by the paralysis.

She still enjoyed arts and crafts, but I worried she might fall and break a hip only to hasten to her passing. Until that day, I suppose my memories must do of us carrying buckets of ripe blackberries through a warm misty rain, and her jubilant face greeting me with a whisper.

"Welcome home, feller …"

Lynn's Thoughts …

Memories are again the center of our story. How do we explain to our little ones what it was like? I remember my grandparents trying to explain what it was like when they were young. And no, they never walked to school uphill both ways. But it was different.

Wild berries are hard to explain. Today, we tell children not to eat anything that is not from a can or a box. Don't drink from that water hose, it's nasty. Stay away from those swings, you'll break your neck.

How do we explain that we pulled apart skates to make a skateboard? We swung from ropes that were older than dirt. Old tires often made for a great escape down a steep slope. And we survived.

The old days … isn't that what they're called?

How do we explain the aroma of fresh, spring grass growing along a well beaten path? I do not believe we can.

Roger, you're showing your age, but we thank you for it.

Shy Boy

Frank Shima

Matt walked into the warm, spring sunshine after his first class of the day – PChem 103.

Just yesterday, he'd been knee-deep in manure, cleaning the gutters at his family farm. Now the aroma of sweet blossoms filled the air at the University of Minnesota. Matt avoided the Vietnam war protesters gathered in front of Coffman Union and walked down the crowded mall, toward Scott Hall. He noticed the girls who exposed as much skin to the warm sun as possible, wearing halter tops and cut-off jeans.

He had been on campus for almost a year and hadn't dated any of these desirable coeds. In that respect, it was no different from high school. Except in high school, he had at least known the girls and knew they'd never date him, even if he asked.

It wasn't like he was unattractive. He was tall and thin with thick, black hair. But here at the University of Minnesota, how was he to meet a girl? It was like the old saying, 'water, water everywhere but not a drop to drink.'

He tried attending college dances, but most girls wouldn't dance with him. Many didn't feel like dancing. If so, why go to a dance? When a girl would dance, it was impossible to talk because the music was so loud. He danced only fast dances where contact wasn't required. Sometimes when his back was turned, the girl would magically disappear before the song was over.

His friend, Dave, at his rooming house, the 1308 Club, had no trouble meeting girls. Matt knew that Dave sneaked girls into his room, a direct violation of Alice's rule thirteen. Matt wouldn't dare break any of Alice's rules, much less rule thirteen.

Matt reached Northrop Auditorium before his next class when a shadow stopped in front of him. He looked up to see an attractive blonde. She pushed a strand of hair from her eyes and smiled.

"Excuse me," she said. "Do you know where Coffman Union is?"

"Ah, sure." Matt pointed at the other end of the mall. "It's that building down there."

"Thanks," she replied but made no movement toward Coffman Union. She shuffled back and forth from one foot to the other.

She glanced up at the lettering CYRUS NORTHRUP MEMORIAL AUDITORIUM that was above the columns. She smiled at Matt before shrugging and blending into the crowd.

Poor kid, he thought. How could anyone not know where Coffman Union was?

Matt scoured the halls of Northrup for a Minnesota Daily. Every bin was empty. The student newspaper would have to pick this day to be late. Then Matt spotted one sitting on the white, wrought iron tables in front of Northrop. Matt hurried over and opened the paper to the personal ads. He frantically searched for his post, scanning the page. Then he found it.

Shy boy wants to meet nice or mod girls. Call Matt at 738-0547.

He cut his final two classes and rushed back to the 1308 Club. By the time he arrived, he was out of breath and sweating. He took the stairs two at a time, eager to check his door. One phone was shared by everyone in the house. If anyone had left a message, a note would be tacked to his door. He turned the corner and didn't know whether to be disappointed or relieved – no messages. He inserted his key into the lock.

"Matt?" That was Alice's voice. "No. He's not here, I told you …"

Matt dropped his books and dashed around the corner.

Alice was on the phone. "A message. You want me to leave a message!"

"Wait!" Matt screamed. "Alice? I'm here!"

Alice glared as she angrily shoved the phone into his hand. "That's the fifth call for you today!"

Matt ignored her and placed the handset to his ear. "Hello?"

"Hi, is this Matt?"

"Ah, yeah."

"I'm Kathy. I saw your ad in the Daily."

"You did?"

"Yes. I'd like to meet you."

"You would?" Matt replied.

Kathy sounded nice. His heart raced as he tried to picture her in his mind.

"Sure. How about tonight?" Kathy suggested.

"Tonight?"

"Yes, tonight."

There was a long pause as Matt tried to figure out what to say next. "Okay. Sure. Tonight. Do you want to see a movie?"

"Movie? Jesus, Matt. You are shy."

"I just thought it'd be a good way to get to know each other," Matt replied.

"Let's not waste any time. How 'bout I come to your place?"

"Ah, no," Matt answered, his face turning red. "I can't have girls in my room, rule thirteen."

"We can't break the rules, can we?" she replied. "Then we'll get a room at the hotel. What do you say?"

"Okay. Where do you live? I'll pick you up."

That was a dumb thing to say. Matt didn't own a car.

"I tell you what ... meet me in the lobby of the Curtis Hotel at seven."

"Okay. But how will I know you?"

"I'll be carrying a red umbrella."

"What if it isn't raining?" Matt asked.

"It doesn't matter."

"Oh, okay, I guess it doesn't."

"And one more thing," she added "I charge fifty dollars. See you at seven, Matt."

"Huh? Wait!" It was too late. Matt stared at the silent handset before hanging up. He looked over at Alice and shrugged.

"No girls in the room!" She turned and stomped down the stairs.

The phone rang again and the call was from a guy pretending to be a girl. Placing the ad had seemed like a good idea at the time, but now Matt wasn't so sure. The response wasn't what he expected.

He headed back to his room to change his clothes. The phone rang again. He would just let someone else answer it. After ten rings, he decided he had better answer the phone. He dashed over just as Alice turned the corner. Matt picked up the receiver.

"Hello, I'd like to talk to Matt."

"This is Matt. This is about the ad, right?"

"I'm Carla. I've been at the university for two years, and I haven't met any boys I like. I'm kinda shy too. I hope that's okay. I mean, the ad said nice or mod girls."

"No, that's fine," Matt replied.

This is more like it, he thought. Unless it's another crank call. "Just so you're not a hooker or a guy or something."

"What do you mean?"

"I'm sorry," Matt continued, "so far I've received calls from a prostitute and from a guy pretending to be a girl."

"That's terrible. I am a girl and definitely not one of those kinds."

"Glad to hear it. I would like to meet sometime. Maybe we could go to a movie."

"I'm sorry," Carla answered. "I can't go to the movies."

"Why not?"

"It's against my religion."

"What kind of religion is that?" Matt asked.

"Southern Baptist. We can't go to dances either. But we could go to church. I think that would be a great way to meet."

"I'm Catholic," Matt answered. "It's against the rules to go to another church."

"I prayed last week for God to send someone to me. I read the ad, and I knew you were the one."

"I'm sure I'm not the one. Goodbye, Carla."

"Goodbye. And I'll pray for you."

The calls continued throughout the day. There were about twenty but none from the perfect girl. Most called out of curiosity, or they were simply kooks. Meeting girls over the phone was proving to be just as difficult as meeting them in person. A rush of calls arrived at midnight, and Alice appeared from out of nowhere with curlers in her hair and a screwdriver in her hand. She disconnected the phone and posted rule fifty-eight – no calls between 10 p.m. and 7 a.m.

The next day, the calls slacked off but each proved to be equally unproductive.

Eventually, he gave the calls over to the other guys, who by this time were quite annoyed. The next call was happily answered by Mike, who accepted a date – a Minnesota Gopher cheerleader. Matt doubted this as he doubted anything Mike had to say. That was until the cheerleader appeared on the doorstep of the 1308 Club asking for Mike.

Soon all the guys had met girls through Matt's ad except Matt. The way things were going, Alice would probably meet a girl before he met one.

Due to the remarkable success of everyone else in the 1308 Club, Matt decided to answer the calls again. That's when he met Gloria. Not in person but in countless hours of phone conversations. She confided in him, telling her innermost secrets. He revealed his feelings – about growing up on the farm – about attending the university with its 40,000 students after graduating from high school in a class of fifty – about the upcoming draft lottery and his thoughts on enlisting and going to Vietnam.

He wanted to meet her, to find out if she matched the perfect picture he had painted in his mind. However, she refused. Was it something about him? Or did she have some grotesquely hideous feature that she was afraid to expose? She always said the time wasn't right for them to meet. Then, when would be the perfect time? For now, he had to be satisfied with the phone calls. What other choice did he have?

On a Saturday night, Dave asked Matt to go to a kegger. Matt reluctantly tagged along. There were always more guys than girls, and he didn't drink beer. He never talked to anyone at parties. Usually, he just sat in a corner observing others having a good time. Sure enough, he ended up in a corner watching everyone else.

Then he heard her voice – Gloria's voice. He was positive. He stood and weaved his way through the crowd toward the sound. Then he saw her. She was gorgeous! Tall, thin, long brown hair that cascaded over her shoulders and down her back. Her eyes were a beautiful brown, and she held a mischievous smile. She was more beautiful than he had imagined. She was surrounded by five guys who looked like they wanted to lure her away into the nearest bedroom. As he neared, he could make out the conversation.

"... and he thought I would go out with him. Do I look like I'm hard up for a date?" She laughed.

The guys laughed too.

"He's a farmer!" she stated.

"Yeah," one of the guys said. "Who knows what he does with those cows and sheep."

A look of disgust spread across Gloria's face as the guy made crude oinking sounds.

"And ..." Gloria continued, "... I make up all this stuff about myself and Matt believes it! How can anyone be so gullible? And so stupid! He's even going to enlist so he can fight in Vietnam."

Matt turned and forced his way through the crowd, trying to block out the laughter. How could she? He stood at the door and his tears welled. He ran into the street unaware of the cold, hard rain plastering his hair and disguising the tears on his cheeks. After passing four blocks, he slowed to a fast walk. Although still crying, he was more angry than hurt. Angry at Gloria. Angry at himself. Angry at the world for creating Gloria and creating him. He sat at a bus stop for what seemed like hours and watched as countless buses splashed by.

"You're wet. Would you like to share my umbrella?" A female voice asked.

Matt looked up and stared at the smiling face peering down at him. Not a red umbrella but a brightly colored paisley one. "Thank you. Not sure if it'll help. I'm already wet."

"You look like a drowned rat," she laughed.

Her statement should have bothered him, but for some strange reason, from this girl it was okay. She was joking with him, not making fun. Matt looked a little more closely at her. She wasn't as beautiful as Gloria. Her eyes weren't as striking. Her hair wasn't as glamorous. But somehow, she was more attractive. Her smile was more comfortable.

"My name's Phyllis," she said, leaning over, trying to hold the umbrella over both of them. Half an umbrella didn't do either much good. She closed her umbrella and sat next to Matt. "May I ask why you're crying?"

Matt told Phyllis about his ad and what happened at the party. Then it hit him – that he was talking to a girl face-to-face. He didn't feel nervous. He didn't stutter or stammer. The things he said somehow made sense. Gloria, in her sick way, had helped him.

"Let's go to Al's Diner," Matt said.

"A cup of coffee will warm us up," she replied.

They stood. Matt took a step and Phyllis laughed.

"Has anyone ever told you that you look like a monkey?"

Matt glanced at his reflection in a nearby store window. "A monkey?" he repeated.

"You remind me of Davy Jones of the Monkees."

Matt laughed. "I do? Wow! Thanks." Matt reached over and took Phyllis's hand. "I think I might cancel my ad in the Daily tomorrow."

Lynn's Thoughts …

Love … and bullying. I do believe they go hand in hand. Maybe not. But it definitely feels like it sometimes.

Frank uniquely captures the environment of college life. If we're not perfect in looks and personality, then more than likely, someone will take advantage of it.

But if we simply just wait, true love eventually crosses our path. We can become so desperate for something that we refuse to wait for the right time … the right place. How do we explain this to others?

In my opinion, most can tell when we're desperate, and it will turn them off. Off from friendships, love, and companionship.

The ending was fabulous. "You remind me of a monkey."

Matt was ready to fight until she clarified that it was a singing band. Too funny.

Great job, Frank. Moral of story … let others finish talking before you jump in head first!

Tia Shanklin

I wish time would stop. I need it to because I have to keep going as long as it keeps going. I just want it to stop so I can relax.

"Sam, can you take out the trash?"

"Oh, Sam! Could you do this project for me, I can't figure it out."

"Sam, you need to put yourself out there so you can get a job."

Always doing what *they* want me to do and not doing what *I* want to do.

What do I want to do?

I suppose I'll do something I like ...

But what do I like?

I've had no time to figure it out. Maybe that's what I can do, figure it out. Try new things. Except that takes time and it's time that I don't have. Because I have to ...

do the dishes

find a job

do my homework

take out the trash

do this sport, no this one

focus on academics, no focus on athletics

focus on your family because we never see you

focus on yourself because you're looking worse for wear

How can I focus on myself when there's no time? Everything is ...

spiraling

spiraling

spiraling

down

down

down

Spiraling into myself and out of myself. What is my self? Who is my self? I need to figure that out, but there is no ...

How do others do this? How do other Sams do this? Am I even Sam? Who is Sam? Who is me? Or am I someone else? Is Sam even real? Yes, Sam has to be real in order to catch up. I try and try, but I can never catch up.

What to do?

SPIRALING

What to do?

I have no clue.

I must find a clue to keep going, but that clue slips down an endless hole that my life created. What do I need to do? Who do I need to be? Wait!

BREATHE

I have to breathe

breathe

breathe

breathe

If I breathe, then I can live, then I can think, then I can ...

DO YOUR WORK!

Right ... **do my work** ...

dishes

job

trash

sports

school

home

friends

When will it stop? So much to do. So much to see. So little time. I must obey ... but why?

Why must I obey?

Obeying takes away time. Should I stop? But if I stop, then others will be upset. Though ... I'm upset. Why can't I decide? Why must it be so hard? Why must time slip away? Wait! I need to stop. All this thinking is taking the time I need to ...

W

O

R

K

Has this happened before? How many times does this happen? I can't recall. Caught in my spiraling consciousness for hours on end, sitting and doing nothing, but thinking. Thinking about everything and nothing at the same time, mixing into static that keeps drowning me.

nothing

everything

nothing

everything

no in-between

Get it together Sam. I must get back to work. Mom'll be upset if I don't and so will Dad.

dishes

work

trash

sports

school

home

friends

Wait ... friends?

Friends are hanging out today!

SPIRALING

I said I would go ... but all this work is taking up my TIME. What do I tell them? They are waiting for me. They'll be upset. Mom and Dad will be upset. I'm upset.

They'll be okay. They'll understand.

But how long will they accept my excuses? How long until they stop inviting me? How long until I have no friends? Then I'll be alone to ...

WORK

WORK

WORK

Until I die.

I don't want to die like that.

What do I do? Who do I upset? Why does the world do this to me? Why do I do this to me? The world spins and spins into the void ...

I fear the void.

I'll never escape the loop of ...

dishes

work

trash

sports

school

home

friends

Me?

When will I be able to focus on me? I'm not the me I want to be. But there's no ...

To become a better me. If I was a better me, I wouldn't be spiraling ...

down

down

down

into the abyss while needing to work and

hang out with friends and keep up with school

and

and

and

and I can't do it anymore. I can't until I'm a me that can be. I can't until I unwind this spiral that knotted itself into my inner being. I can't do it with just me. I have to do it with ... we.

We ... yes.

That's it.

A beam cuts through the spiral of my soul. If there is a we, I can find me. If I can find another, then me becomes we, and I can breathe without squeezing my lungs. This is the first time I can see past the spiral. The first time climbing out of the hole. The first time that 

has no hold. Can I find the me?

I just have to try.

Lynn's Thoughts …

As a college professor of literature, I related to this piece. Not to mention that I truly enjoyed formatting it. It is not often that I run across true prose in its most simplest of form.

Between the lines, Tia explains what it is like being young. Told to do several things at once, mixing life with friends and school, the turmoil ensues.

Some say that being young is a blessing. Yes … and no. Health may be more energetic, but the mind refuses to relent. Everything flows through the ears or the eyes or the lips. With enhanced senses, at times, life can be too much and our world spirals. With nothing but flashes of light and sound, how is anyone supposed to function?

Tia has a lot to say in this piece.

THE GLITCH

Arthur M. Doweyko

Hadley Banes usually walked with his head down after work – onto Fifth Street, right on MacKenzie, and two blocks to his apartment. During rush hour one didn't try to make new friends.

Today was different.

Hadley was just discharged from the Emergency Room with a nasty head injury. It happened at his work – a dumb move to hurry down the stairs that ended up more like a swan dive to the basement.

A wagging ponytail some five paces ahead caught his eye. As he watched the mesmerizing sway, the man who owned it disappeared – poof! – gone! And no one seemed to notice.

Hadley stopped walking, blinked his eyes, and massaged his bandage, attempting to quell the headache now threatening to erupt into a monsoon. A good squeeze of his eyes brought the ponytail man back, walking only a few paces ahead as if nothing had happened.

Hadley shook his head and started up again, trying to ignore a growing disquiet in his gut. Home was only a few blocks off. It happened again.

Only this time, a woman with a skirt a couple sizes too small careened past. In mid-sashay, she simply vanished. Hadley stopped, this time looking around, praying for a witness.

"Did you see that?" he asked a fellow with a newspaper tucked under an arm.

The man opted for a wide berth, picking up his pace.

Some ten yards ahead of the newspaper man, the woman reappeared. Once again, no one seemed to either notice, or maybe worse, to care.

Hadley considered catching up to the woman, to ask if she experienced anything unusual. He began to jog when he heard a voice.

"Don't bother." The voice came from the entrance to a small, city park. An older man with graying hair, wearing a dark suit sat at a bench, feeding pigeons from a paper bag. Nearby, a policeman leaned against the gate. A little girl in a teal-colored hoodie, maybe seven- or eight-year-old, stood between them, staring at Hadley.

He took a step. "Excuse me, did you say something?"

"Don't bother," the girl repeated. "Chasing that woman, I mean. I noticed the same thing."

The girl's penetrating stare had Hadley transfixed. "What did you see?" He gave both the pigeon and the policeman a glance, worried they'd wonder about his sanity.

"I saw the glitch," the girl replied.

"You're awfully young to wander about alone." Hadley asked the young girl, "Where are your parents?"

The girl nodded at the bench. "My grandpa, George. He's almost blind. We come to the park sometimes."

Hadley turned to look at the policeman, but he was gone.

The girl laughed. "He just left. That was Officer Wilson. He patrols the park."

Hadley let out a sigh of relief. "What's your name?"

"Brady, like the Patriots' quarterback."

"Nice. My name's Hadley. Did you see the woman disappear and then come back?"

"Just like the guy with the ponytail."

"And how come no one else notices?" Hadley wasn't sure why he asked. After all, she was just a child. What could she know? What could anyone know?

"Because we're special. You hurt your head. Maybe you've got a brain aneurysm."

"That may be, but what about you?"

"I had an operation." Brady lowered her hoodie, exposing a bald spot sporting a curved, crimson scar.

"I'm sorry."

"They got most of it. Two months ago. My grandpa said we should spend more time together." The little girl flicked back up her hoodie. "I see you've never seen the glitch before."

"Sometimes, I don't pay attention and think I might have seen something odd. Maybe it's just my imagination, but when I look again –"

Brady spread out her arms. "You see everything's as it should be."

Hadley nodded and wondered about the girl. She'd seen what he'd seen but wasn't confused. She looked like a first grader but spoke like an adult.

"Now you're wondering about me. I'm too smart for my age, right?"

"That's right," Hadley replied. "You do come across that way."

Brady pointed to her head. "It happened after the operation."

"Mind if I sit?"

The old man nodded at Hadley's question. "Please do. I see you're enjoying a conversation with my granddaughter."

Hadley tip-toed past the throng of pigeons and sat. When Brady nudged herself between the two, he replied, "She's quite bright."

"That she is. But sometimes she makes things up, don't you Brady?"

Brady winked at Hadley. "That's true. I enjoy make-believe."

Hadley laughed. "Children do that sometimes."

Brady smiled. "Let's just watch the people walk by for a while."

Such an odd thing to suggest, but Hadley agreed. They sat in silence, staring at the passing parade of people. When two women flickered out, he felt a nudge on his ribs.

Brady whispered, "See that?"

Hadley nodded, and as they watched, three more suffered the same existential wink.

"You seem okay with this," Hadley stated.

Brady replied, "That's because I figured it out."

"Oh? What do you think it is?"

"The machine is old and breaking down."

"What machine?"

George chuckled. "She's doing it again. Don't let her get you going."

Brady nodded. "The machine that runs the world."

"Like in the movies?" Hadley added. "Like – "

George interrupted. "I don't think any movie had a machine running everything."

"Maybe you're right," Hadley replied. "Where did you get such an idea?"

George chuckled again. "Too much TV. Brady, I think it's time for us to go home."

"Yes, Grandpa." Brady took the old man's hand and the two stood.

Hadley, who remained seated, said, "Why are you so sure about that machine?"

As the pair winded their way to the park's entrance, Brady turned and replied, "I found it. I can show you."

By the time Hadley had digested the comment, the two had already left, being swallowed by the twilight.

Hadley closed the door to his apartment, taking care to slide several extra bolts into place. With a beer in his hand, he settled onto his couch and switched on the TV. He watched the news for an hour. No one flickered in or out. After his second beer, his head pounded. He popped a pain pill. Maybe he imagined today, maybe even the little girl. He propped up a pillow behind his head and closed his eyes.

Hadley woke to the sunlight streaming through a break in the curtains, or maybe it was to the sound of a passing siren, or a car horn – city sounds normal for a city morning. As his sleepy brain shifted into gear, he realized it was Friday and he was late for work. He sprung off the couch a bit too fast and had to pause while fighting off a bout of nausea. His fingers ran through his thinning hair, confirming that the bandage was still there. He already had his shoes on, so he fumbled with the locks on his door and loped down the stairs.

The fresh air felt good. At the park, no old man, no policeman, and no little girl waited for him. Just the same, he chose to focus on the sidewalk for fear of seeing something abnormal. He slipped into McCray's Department Store, hoping to reach the back office without being spotted.

"Oh, hi, Mr. Banes." The aging spinster at the perfume station waved, giving him her morning's wide smile.

He summoned up a polite nod. "Miss Salesbury."

"Mr. Corns would like to see you."

Hadley felt a vacuum suck in his gut. Mr. Corns had a thing about time, more specifically being on it.

He knocked on the manager's door and was invited in. "Sit down, Hadley."

Mr. Corns sat back in his overstuffed leather chair, swinging it to and fro.

"Sir?"

Mr. Corns glanced at his watch. "Two hours late."

"My accident … yesterday, sir. I had to visit the Emergency Room, and they –"

Mr. Corns' face turned red.

Hadley continued. "… ten stitches." He reached into his jacket pocket. "And these pain pills, and …"

Mr. Corns disappeared. Only his voice lingered, "And … and …"

Hadley tried to ignore the empty chair. After a few moments, he stood and waved a hand over Mr. Corns' chair, confirming that the man was gone, not just invisible.

He opened the office door and peeked out. Customers still wandered down the aisles as usual. Miss Salesbury threw him her morning smile, but this time it was a bit more pronounced.

He turned back to check on Mr. Corns.

"Is everything alright, Mr. Banes?" Miss Salesbury stepped around her station.

Hadley closed the door behind him. "Why, yes, Miss Salesbury. No problem at all. Need to get to my office. Lots of work to do." He ignored her confused expression and quick-stepped to the back of the store. When he opened his office door, the man seated at his desk pushed up his glasses and said, "What can I do for you, Mr. Banes?"

Hadley felt the blood drain from his face. He stared at Mr. Corns for a few seconds. "Sorry, sir. I'm not sure –"

"That's quite alright, Mr. Banes. I'll have those figures for you before noon. Is there anything else you need?"

Hadley leaned back and checked the name on the door. Maybe he was still at Mr. Corns' office. Yep, it was Corns' name on the door, but with the title of Accountant – his title.

He forced out a reply. "Not at this time, sir … ah, Mr. Corns."

When he returned to the manager's office, the door plate read "Mr. Hadley Banes – Manager." He cracked open the door and peeked inside – still empty. Naturally, he thought that since this was now his office, perhaps he was the manager. He walked toward the front of the store.

Miss Salesbury paused, talking to a customer, beaming. "Have a good day, Mr. Banes."

"I … I'll be back after lunch, Miss Salesbury."

His head pounded. On the way home, the image of the little girl in a hoodie flashed across his mind. She had said something important. A policeman standing at the park's entrance nodded as he passed. He knew the officer's name. How did he know that?

"Officer Wilson, is that right?"

"Yes, sir. How are you today?"

"Okay, I guess." Hadley glanced down and only a few pigeons landed on the empty bench.

"Not here today," Officer Wilson stated.

"What was that?"

The officer shrugged. "Brady and her grandfather. The two you sat with yesterday. They are not here today."

Had it been only yesterday? "Oh, yes."

Officer Wilson frowned. "Brady, the little girl, she's a fireplug."

Hadley remembered the teal hoodie. "That she is."

"Too bad about her."

"What do you mean?"

"Her grandfather told me they took her to hospital … Grace Memorial on the other side of the park."

"She told me she had an operation."

"Yeah, she's a trooper. Some kind of relapse," he said.

"Grace Memorial?"

Hadley darted past Officer Wilson. He wasn't sure why, but he felt a kinship with that little girl. They had experienced the disappearing people together. 'A glitch,' she called it. And … a machine. She was in trouble.

He reached the hospital entrance, forcing himself to slow down his breathing. "Excuse me … I'm here to … see a little girl … her first name's Brady. I don't know her last."

The red-haired woman raised her head above the edge of her monitor. "Sir, you'll have to give me more information than that. You're clearly not a relative."

"No, I'm a friend."

The woman's head dipped out of sight. After a few moments of tapping, she reappeared. "She was admitted yesterday afternoon. However, I cannot allow you to visit her. She's in ICU. Immediate family only."

Hadley's shoulders slump. "Can I just sit here and wait?"

"Certainly, but only for a while. That's our waiting area, and we have a lot of people on the weekends."

Hadley found an empty seat. His eyes focused on the dull gray tile. Moments later they closed, and he could see Brady with her knowing look. Together, they watched people disappear and reappear. She laughed and explained that it was all because of a machine, a very old machine that was running down.

Someone kicked his foot. "Looks like you were daydreaming."

Hadley brushed a finger over his eyes. "George? It's George, right?"

"Last I checked. What brings you here?"

"To be honest, I don't know. I take that back. Your granddaughter, Brady … the park cop, Wilson, said she was –"

"She's here. She passed out yesterday. The doctors said the tumor was back, growing fast this time."

"Did they operate?"

"I'm afraid not." George's voice sounded thin. "There's nothing they can do."

"There must be something. A specialist? Some drug?"

"They've got the best here on staff."

A silence fell between them.

"You want to see her?" George asked.

"She's in ICU. They said only immediate family."

"Come with me. I think she'd be happy to see you."

George took Hadley by the hand, using the other on his cane for support. They arrived at the receptionist arm in arm. "This is my brother," George said. "We're here to see my granddaughter, Brady. She's in ICU."

The woman gave Hadley a long look. "I don't believe you." She muttered as she scribbled something on a pad and handed it to Hadley. "Go ahead, George, make sure he stays with you."

George gave her a polite nod, and minutes later the two were on the top floor negotiating the color-coded corridors.

A passing nurse paused to whisper, "She's asleep."

George nodded. "We just want to look in on her."

Two doors down, Hadley's jaw dropped as they stepped into a dark cavern. A row of beds was lined against the wall. Only one was occupied.

A subdued light silhouetted canyons of equipment surrounding the tiny bed. Beeping and clicking filled the otherwise mind-numbing silence.

Little Brady was cocooned in white linens. A tube ran from her nose to one of the behemoth machines while a set of wires snaked up from under the linens to a monitor. An IV bag hung alongside her bed, glowing in the indirect lighting. Each drop seemed to pause before being sent into her bloodstream.

George sat on the only chair beside the bed. "She was in a coma until a few hours ago. You can talk to her." The old man wiped away a tear. "She'd like that."

Hadley inched closer until he hovered above her face. Brady's eye and lips were coated with something shiny. The monitor displayed heart and breathing rhythms. Both seemed slow.

He leaned closer and whispered, "Brady, can you hear me? Something happened. My boss … well he disappeared, and when he showed up, he had my job, and … well, now I'm the boss. At least that's what I think. I'm really not sure what's going on." He felt guilty pressing her for answers while she lay there, helpless.

"I'm going out for a moment." George shuffled off, closing the door behind him.

"I can hear you," Brady whispered.

Hadley reared back, almost falling to a knee. He chuckled.

Brady gazed at him from the edge of the bed cover. "Are you alright?"

"That's a question I should be asking you."

"I know I'm not okay. As a matter of fact, I don't think I'll be around much longer."

"Don't say that. There's always hope."

"Not for me." She pouted as her own words sunk in. After a moment, she said, "So, you like what I did?"

"What do you mean?"

"The machine. I saw it better than ever. You can see it too if you try."

"Brady, that's just your imagination."

"It's here, you know …" – she pointed to her head – "… just concentrate."

Hadley shut his eyes and cleared his mind.

"Open your eyes, silly."

He tried picturing something huge, something with lots of dials, and gears, and moving parts. Nothing. No, wait. For a second a set of bluish lines appeared above the bed. Then they were gone. His head pounded again.

"You saw it. I know you saw it." Brady beamed.

"I saw something."

"Blue, right?"

He nodded.

"I can see it without trying."

"Describe it to me."

"It's bigger than this room … bigger than the whole city, maybe as big as the universe."

"Go on."

"There are these wires or strings … they're sort of attached to everything, even to people."

"And you can touch them?"

Brady's eyes flickered and closed. The beeping from one of the instruments nearby sounded louder.

A nurse rushed in through the door with George close behind. She elbowed Hadley to the side and said, "You'll have to leave now. She needs her rest."

Hadley backed away as George tugged at his elbow.

Hadley threw an empty beer can across his living room. He downed a painkiller and eased himself onto the couch. Brady's machine – had he seen it? The dim room offered no clue. He tried imagining those blue lines. Nothing.

The next morning, Sunday morning, he changed his shirt and headed out to the hospital. The sun had been up for hours and was now intense. Pigeons surrounded the empty bench at the park, pecking the ground as if searching for the remains of the seeds from the day before.

The hospital receptionist was new. "Can I help you?"

"I'm a very close friend of the little girl in ICU. Her name is Brady … I'd like to stop in a moment to see how she's doing."

The spectacled blue-haired volunteer frowned. "Did you say ICU?"

"Yes, she's the only one up there … at least as of yesterday."

"I'm sorry, sir, we do have one patient in ICU, but he's a 70-year-old cardiac case."

Fearing the answer, Hadley stuttered, "Was the girl released?"

"You said her name is Brady?"

Hadley nodded as a few more keys tapped out a rhythm. "There's no record of anyone but the cardiac patient up there for the last two days." After a few more taps, she added, "No Brady in the system, anywhere in the hospital. You sure you have the right place?"

Hadley looked about the waiting room. "This is the right hospital. What the hell is going on? She was here yesterday. I was here yesterday. The red head who was here … she would remember me … we had a – "

"Sorry, sir, but I was here yesterday, and I don't remember you."

The words rattled inside Hadley's head like a loose chain. "I don't understand." His headache was back. As he turned away, the receptionist bade him a good day.

He spotted a familiar face at the park entrance.

"Officer Wilson, how's it going?"

The officer dipped his cap. "Fine. Beautiful day, right?"

"I wish it was. That little girl, Brady … I visited her at the hospital yesterday. She wasn't doing too well. And now, they tell me they don't have any record of her being there."

Wilson took his cap off and brushed his hand over his brow. "Little girl? What little girl?"

"Yeah … the one I talked to the day before. Remember the old man and the pigeons? Hell, yesterday you told me she was in the hospital." Hadley felt the sidewalk wavering beneath his feet.

"I'm sorry, sir. I don't recall. 'Sides, I don't believe we've met."

Hadley took a few steps back and slumped onto the bench.

"Are you all right? You're looking a little pale."

Hadley fought back the urge to scream. First, the hospital and now the policeman. Had he been dreaming this whole time? "Just need a minute …" He massaged his bandage. "Got this bump the other day."

Wilson nodded. "Take your time. I'm here if you need me."

Hadley kept his eyes focused on the people passing by. Sure enough, one disappeared and reappeared a few seconds later. Brady, the phantom little girl, had called it a glitch. Maybe she was something he imagined helping him cope with his vision problems. That's it. His injured brain came up with all of it. In any event, tomorrow was another day – back to work managing the store. Things would settle down. He'd become normal again. He was sure of it.

Twelve years later …

Hadley woke to a familiar sound – beeping. A light from somewhere off to his left cut into the darkness. He was on his back and the light was coming from several nearby instruments. A bed sheet pressed down on his chest. He was tucked in good.

He tried to call out but gagged on a tube in his throat. As he fought back an urge to vomit, he recognized the room – ICU. But why was he here?

As if in answer, the door swung open followed by a shadow outlined in the fluorescent's lights. When the door closed the visitor blended into the dull gray walls.

"Who's here? What happened?" The words were garbled, he didn't believe the person would understand.

A hand appeared before his face. "Easy, now. I'm taking your tube out."

The voice was female. After a quick tug, he coughed. "Thanks. Do you know why I'm here?"

A soft light flickered on, and a blurred image of a nurse's cap loomed into view.

"The doctor placed you here for observation. He'll be in shortly to discuss your progress."

Hadley rummaged through his tattered memories. He had just left his retirement party at the store. He remembered walking past the park feeling a bit light-headed and sitting on the bench near the entrance. That's it. Nothing more.

"Just you rest now. The doctor will be with you shortly." The nurse vanished through the door.

Odd thing, Hadley thought – being in the exact same hospital where he had last seen the little girl. So long ago. Maybe this was the same bed. But that was all a delusion brought about by his head injury, wasn't it? People stopped disappearing years ago. The door swung wide, and someone entered.

"I'm Dr. Ben. I hear you're feeling better, Mr. Banes."

"I suppose."

"Who took your endotracheal tube out?"

"The nurse … she was just here."

"We'll get you a nasal tube. I'll let her know. Now, to the point, you had a stroke, Mr. Banes. Do you have any relatives we should contact?"

"Eh … no, I live alone … a couple of blocks from here."

The doctor lifted the bed sheet at his feet. "Can you move your toes?"

After a moment, the doctor pulled back the sheet over Hadley's arms. "How about your fingers?"

Hadley tried moving everything.

The doctor shook his head. "You can never tell about these things."

"What does that mean?"

"At the moment, you are paralyzed, Mr. Banes."

Hadley took a moment to take in the news.

"Don't fret, Mr. Banes," the doctor replied. "We've seen many cases like yours. There's always a chance you'll get back some of your movement. I'll return later with a physical therapy plan for you. And I'll send that nurse in to set you up with oxygen."

The doctor receded into the darkness. The door opened and closed.

Hadley pressed his eyes closed and sprung them open. He was still in bed with that incessant beeping. Today was real. He was in trouble. His mind swept through all the things he needed to do – there weren't many.

"I've got to get out of here."

"Don't bother." The nurse had returned. As she leaned over, his eyes cleared to see her smile. Her long blonde locks peeked out from under the blue cap.

"Why are you smiling like that?"

She tossed her head back and giggled. "You don't recognize me?"

Her face wavered, becoming a little girl's face for a moment. "It's not possible. Brady? You … you weren't real. I came back to see you, but no one knew anything."

"And you thought it was all because of that bump on your head."

"That's right. And now, I don't know what to think."

"You're here, paralyzed. That's real enough, right?"

"Yeah. Real enough." Hadley's head sagged into his pillow.

"Don't be so sad."

He stared at the girl who could not be.

"Remember the machine?"

Hadley nodded.

"I can still see it."

"So?"

Brady drew closer and grasped Hadley's wrist. "You can see it too. I know you can."

"All I see is the end. Don't get me wrong, Brady, but there's nothing left. You have everything to look forward to. Just let me be. What will happen will happen."

"That's not exactly true."

Hadley felt pressure on his wrist and the room darkened even more.

"What are you doing?"

"Just watch."

At first, he only saw her dim outline. Then her cap seemed to float above her head. A bluish aura appeared like a halo and descended over her body. "Do you see it, Hadley?"

"I see a blue light."

"There's more.

The glow gradually coalesced, forming shapes – blurred figures, lines reaching out from each of them and going off in every direction.

"What the hell?"

"It's the machine, Hadley. And you're in it. I'm in it. Everybody and everything is in it."

"What does that mean?

"It means you can choose," she said.

"I don't understand."

"You can pick a different reality. Look!" Brady swung her arm, and the room filled with music as if she was playing a harp. A myriad of human shapes rained down around them.

Hadley gasped. "That's me! And you! There are so many of us."

"Look closely and choose Hadley. There's no need to accept your present fate."

The cascade continued, flashing by versions of himself and Brady. His mind jerked on a string, and a figure came into focus. "There's one that could work."

"Are you sure?"

Hadley remained unconvinced but was willing to play. "Life's an adventure. Why not?"

The room filled with color, hummed, and then everything fell black.

Hadley stood on his tippytoes to look over the windowsill.

Madam Portknockie placed a hand on his shoulder. "Are you excited?"

He'd only been in the orphanage for about a week before being told there might be a chance for him to be adopted.

Portknockie moved the curtain to the side. "Looks like they're here."

A shiny black Rolls pulled up to the curb. The chauffer opened the rear door, and a stately and finely dressed woman stepped out. As she looked at the orphanage, her gaze paused at Hadley's window.

Madame Portknockie waved. "That's Lady Grace Remington. That handsome fellow is Lord Charles Remington. They're one of the richest families in Scotland." She allowed the curtain to fall back into place, grabbing Hadley by the hand. "Let's go meet them."

Being only eight years old, Hadley had to skip alongside Portknockie just to keep up. They arrived at the front door as the Remington's ascended the stone steps.

Madame Portknockie said, "Welcome Lord Remington, Lady Remington. I trust you had a pleasant journey?"

Lord Remington nodded. "Most pleasant. And this is?"

"May I introduce Master Hadley. He's been eagerly looking forward to making your acquaintance."

Inside the foyer, the Remington's were ushered to a plush divan set against one of the walls. Portknockie positioned Hadley in the center of an oval rug and stated, "What do you think?"

Lady Remington held up her spectacles and bent over to take a closer look. A move that made Hadley feel like he was a store display.

"Fine looking boy," she said. "Is he intelligent?"

Hadley spoke up. "Pleased to meet you, Lady Remington. And you, Lord Remington. I can count and love to read and learn new things. I'm sure I will be an asset to your family."

Lady Remington gasped. "My, my, marvelous language skills."

Lord Remington nodded. "A smart one."

A week later, Hadley waved goodbye to Madame Portknockie from the rear window of the Remington's Rolls. He was off to a new life.

The steady purr of the automobile tugged at his eyelids. His mind drifted, letting faded memories of a past life drift along the blur of passing trees and farmlands. Fleeting glimpses of a young, precocious girl haunted each frame of his reverie.

"Wake up, Master Hadley." The chauffer smiled and said, "You're here, time to meet your new family."

Hadley clambered out of the Rolls onto a gravel drive. A brisk wind accented with the woody scent of heather washed over him as he gazed up at an enormous house – a house of tall windows and doors. A small group standing out front.

Lady Remington stepped forward and said, "Master Hadley, may I present you with our household?" She announced the name and function of each person from butler to cook. Each bowed in turn.

A breeze fingered its way under Hadley's shirt, scooting a chill up his back. His lips trembled as he felt both welcomed and acutely alone.

The moment Lady Remington finished her introductions, a little girl squeezed through the assembly. She sported a familiar wide grin and long, curly blonde hair with a bright, teal-colored ribbon. "Hi, Hadley!"

Lynn's Thoughts …

The Glitch, a great sci-fi that could possibly be expanded into a novel.

Arthur creates a second reality where out lives are directed by a machine. AI again, entering our lives? My question … does the little girl flip time to help the old man? Or does she allow him to die with dignity?

This short story mixes realism with fantasy, and the resulting illusion is one to make a person think. What is real? What is fake? How much credence do we give to what our senses experience?

The story delves much deeper than into someone who works everyday and visits a park occasionally. It is a question of whether or not our reality is anything more than a computer matrix. A matrix that can glitch …

Arthur's world of illusion captures the reader and actually hands us a questionnaire. A list of questions to decipher about our lives. If there were a machine … would you push the button?

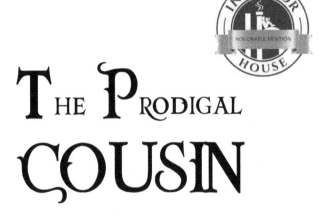

The Prodigal Cousin

Gary Girzadas

My mom placed a three-quart Calphalon pot on the electric range and spun the dials with an alert flick of the wrist. She shuffled through the kitchen, piecing together yet another meal, dragging the ends of her terrycloth robe with a heavy grace.

I stepped into the dim light of the early morning kitchen. Drawn to the clattering sounds, I looked down at the large bowl. Oatmeal never looked appetizing first thing in the morning - the pale water, the oats, a slab of butter, a sprinkle of salt floating lifeless above the heat.

I hate oatmeal.

My father was never around in the mornings. He would wake early and leave. Some odd transformation occurred in the pre-dawn hours that I never had the privilege to witness. What did he wear to work? Blue jeans? Scrubs? A sports coat?

What did successful surgeons wear? They woke early like fishermen, and before their brains kicked in, were gone. Instead of Chryslers or Hondas like most, doctors drove Mercedes or BMWs. Occasionally, a particularly iconoclastic ophthalmologist drove a Lexus but this was before Lexus became popular.

Doctors drove to the hospital with a sense of determination to don their white coats and scrubs, and little, blue paper skull caps. They vaguely reminded me of fighter pilots. I imagined them greeted by doating nurses and administrative staff smiling with their stout confidence. Occasionally, I heard my father's keys as he left, but I never actually saw him.

I sat at the end of the large family table and stared at my oatmeal. The forlorn mixture was always transformed by my mother into a bountiful feast. The oats took on a new life, bursting with steam and texture. The melted margarine - butter was outlawed by my family - and brown sugar melted together creating a rich concoction. She added fresh strawberries slices coated with sugar and cinnamon raisin toast. All topped off with a glass of apple juice.

I ate in blissful ignorance. Whatever happened yesterday and whatever was coming never entered the equation. It was the late eighties and the Soviet Union was quiet, and we hadn't yet been bombarded with smart phones or school shootings. Climate change wasn't invented yet, and the only existential threat we faced was that one day the sun would run out of fuel. But that wouldn't happen for billions of years.

I ate my sumptuous oatmeal confident in the sun's power, glancing out the windows as the predawn light rose through the trees.

School in those days existed on a neutral plane. It was before the meteoric decline of the church, and Catholic schools with their Catholicism were at their zenith in the southern suburbs of

Chicago. These neighborhoods south of 87th street and beyond the cemeteries and forest preserves were a network of parishes, named for obscure saints, filled with chummy priests, stingy nuns, and kids - lots of kids. The nuns where still young, not yet in their eighties. Although mature, they were also spry and secure. They were sharp-looking in a *don't screw with me, kid* kind of way. Austere and worldly at the same time. They had eschewed their habits in a sort of nod to modernity and seemed more respectable for it.

As I skated through my classes, secure in the knowledge that one day I would be a professional athlete or doctor, the nuns became stage props in the larger world. They were imposing and controlling but stayed on the sidelines - for the most part. The constant thought *I should be doing something* hadn't yet entered the frame, but it was revving up in the back of mind.

One day, my cousin Jerry arrived. It was on a Sunday evening of meatloaf and mashed potatoes. We had run out of ketchup. Therefore, tomato sauce was slathered across my plate. After dinner, we said our usual goodbyes to Grandma Helen and Uncle Pete. Jerry, oddly enough, did not put on his coat. His mom, my Aunt Judy, stood wrapped in her sweater and scarf, her shoulders hunched as if to brace for a hardy goodbye. Jerry stood firm between the kitchen and family room beneath the heavy exposed beams. He did not move.

Some agreement was made, some words exchanged, and the heavy door closed behind my aunt. Jerry stood quietly with his blond hair that was straight and thick like a California beach bum. It was trimmed in a bowl cut that waved in unison when he turned his head. My dad did all the talking. He papered over the situation with a few thick platitudes. My sister showed Jerry to the smallest bedroom upstairs, the one with a crank-out window that looked over the shed and gardens.

My aunt's house in Evergreen Park was much different than ours. It had a big wooden K on the front – a tribute to their last name, Kowalski. A small, detached garage and alley where the garbage was collected. The small kitchen had a little circular table where they ate with their cats. Breakfast was cereal or pop tarts and sometimes eggs and bacon. In the middle of the house, a former study was turned into a display for guns that lined in racks surrounding the room, along with bayonets and Vietnam artifacts and mementos like lighters, letters, and photos. When Uncle Mike was tinkering with his cars, Jerry would sneak into that room, dreaming of becoming a Marine. He wanted to make Uncle Mike proud.

Jerry was received somewhat like a foreigner in my suburban world. First and foremost, he was adopted. A transfer student was one thing, but a transfer student from an unknown origin was quite another. Second, his mom had been recently divorced from my uncle. To my nuclear family, divorce seemed like a big deal. And then … Jerry didn't play golf or video games. It seemed like he had to learn everything from scratch, which made me feel ashamed and sad. Later in life, Jerry's left arm would sport an oversized Motley Crue tattoo. Later in life, he would learn to love muscle cars and shoot pool. But that winter, while living under our roof, he was an awkward blond kid who didn't talk much, eat much, or shower much.

The next morning - Jerry's first experience attending Catholic school - every light in the house was on. Even the big chandelier that we had to clean once a year was blaring above the kitchen table. It felt like we were about to go on a family vacation or something. Everyone was awake and running around. Jerry, wearing dark blue pants and a light blue uniform shirt borrowed from my older brother Jason, sat quietly at the table. He didn't own any dress shoes so he wore his white gym sneakers. His hair was combed, and for the first time, his forehead was actually visible. He looked thin but appeared as a respectable new student.

Because Jerry and I were almost the same age, I was the one to walk him to school. The two of us probably looked strange as we trekked along the quiet streets. We passed through the neighbor's tennis courts and the open lot owned by a local dentist. We traced the line of the creek past the viaduct where catfish lived in the murky gray water. We didn't speak much.

"Are the teachers nice?" he eventually asked in his low baritone voice.

I didn't know what to say. They were, of course, not nice. The nuns were harsh and vindictive except for the occasional soft soul who'd been there forever. I didn't want to color his experience of the first day, so I replied, "Yeah, they're pretty nice."

We entered the school, and I bid my goodbyes. Jerry entered the office and stood with a chagrined look while employees introduced themselves. I lingered, watching through the sliding glass window. The glances from the staff as they assessed this new creature seemed as if they understood he was trouble. Afterall, his admission was a favor to my parents. An indulgence for their years of support as coaches, chaperones, ushers. The respectability factor many churches so desperately relied on.

That first day Jerry was a novelty. In every seventh-grade class he had to introduce himself.

"Jerry Kowalski."

He pronounced his name with a flat factuality of a soldier stating his rank. He didn't have the lilting names of the other classmates. They were athletes and budding actors with names like D.J. Bentoloma and Nicolette Ferrara. Even Charlotte Blanc's name had a vaguely culinary appeal. Jerry Kowalski was a name too old for the seventh grade. Today, he would be known as a Gerald,

James, or Jack. But back then, he was just Jerry. An odd boy from another world.

He made it through the first day on the fumes of politeness. We walked home along the ice, etching footprints in the snow. I looked over at Jerry, and he was waving a stick against the banks. I imagined his life story - perhaps a teen mother who worked as a back-up singer for a manipulative nightclub manager. No love, no ceremony, just intoxicated and poor judgment. This was the story I had concocted for my cousin. In truth, Jerry's parents were a hard-working Ukrainian couple whose families immigrated to Chicago in the twenties. They worked for Wieboldt's and International Harvester for many years. His father, a strong honest man, was called back to Ukraine to help fight the Russians during a crisis and never returned.

It was at the Nativity Church orphanage where my aunt had found Jerry and was immediately struck by his blond hair. Blonde like hers. She adopted him probably wanting to make amends for giving up her biological daughter many years earlier. Her heart was seeking to make things right in an asymmetrical world, compensating for guilt, masking her past sins.

However, the nuns too were compensating. They were trying to rid the world of its ambiguities. They were ambitious individuals who bought into a code of conduct and community that many didn't understand or follow. They were trying to right a ship that in their minds had gone horribly off course. Into this world of black and white, good and bad, entered my cousin, Jerry Kowalski. A cousin with no past and an uncertain future.

For Jerry, there were no ambiguities. He didn't have to change in his world. He was virtuous by just being true to his personal instincts. The nuns may have been reshaping souls, raising future dentists and pharmacists, but Jerry's future was already sealed. He was a Marine in waiting. He refused to believe in their lies.

Jerry was in his social studies class led by the notorious Mrs. Sims and was asked to recite his essay about the executive branch - say something smart to the class. Jerry was not much of a political science student. He was supposed to have said whether a president's personal life affected their public policies. Did it matter if a president was divorced or had an affair? If yes, should we believe they were still worthy of such a high office? Jerry didn't understand the concept. He stood and stated that the president was a private individual. He stated that President Reagan didn't like people in his personal business because he was the president and should not have to share his most intimate secrets. It was the words intimate secrets that did my cousin in. The class snickered and Jerry's face flushed.

Mrs. Sims was a notorious battle-axe in those days. She said he couldn't return to his seat. Jerry refused to stand in front of the other students and be chastised. She was not a nun but should have been. Jerry defiantly walked back to his seat and mumbled something derisive.

The word *bitch* was the questionable one. It was the word that became the bone of contention. It was the word that Jerry insisted he never said. But a word Mrs. Sims most definitely remembered. It was a word that was credited with keeping him out of school and sending him back to Evergreen Park.

Jerry was transferred between public schools for many years after that. First to Carl Sandberg and then to Alan Shepherd and finally to Evergreen Park Academy. He never graduated but eventually settled for his GED. There was a collective family sigh of relief when he passed, and they shipped him off to the world. He would take his certificate of general educational development and become a newspaper delivery person until his car broke down. Later he became an Amazon warehouse employee. Ultimately, he married a kind woman who was certified as a Wicca Priestess. They lived across the border in Illinois, collecting welfare checks as he worked odd jobs. The Marines never called. Although, he did use his dial-up internet to search for his real parents.

The day after my cousin was kicked out of Saint Albert's, life at school seemed to return to normal. The school's green walls somehow became more cheerful. The snow dropped gracefully on the courtyard, collecting on the sleeves of Mary giving solemnity to her outstretched hands.

One morning while in home room, the buzzer rang and the loudspeaker clicked to life. I was being called to the office. My heart sank. I didn't know if I was in trouble or being questioned about Jerry. I was, after all, his cousin.

I entered the office with anxious hands clasped into fists. Flowers had been placed in a glass vase on the counter, and I thought I might knock them over. The principal sat behind her large desk speaking on the phone behind a closed, glass door.

Is she speaking to my parents?

The secretary stood. "I wish I had your mother," she stated with mock sarcasm. She stretched out her hand and held up the familiar sight of a fast-food happy meal. The smile of Ronald McDonald gleamed as relief ran through my body. The principal peered through the glass and gave me an uncharacteristic smile.

I turned to leave with my lunch.

"Wait!" the secretary stated.

She produced a cardboard tray stacked with a pile of French fries. "Your mom brough enough for the whole class."

I carried the bounty to my classroom feeling somewhat embarrassed. One by one, the students walked forward and grabbed their prize like greedy little pirates. For some odd reason, the tangy fries tasted doubly delicious in school. We ate as the teacher resumed the lesson. It was something about verb endings.

I returned home exhausted. All I wanted was to shoot some baskets and allow the day to fall behind me. But my parents had said to include Jerry as much as possible.

Where was Jerry, anyway?

I searched the basement and the bedrooms. Nothing. He had cleaned out his small room, and the uniform was draped over the edge of the bed. My brothers were at practice and my mom was at the store. My father was at work. I grabbed a can of Pringles and glanced out the back door. Sitting on the screened porch was Jerry's suitcase and backpack.

Was he leaving?

On the table was a pen next to a pad of paper but nothing was written on it. I walked out and headed into the woods. There on the trails, where we rode bikes or blew off firecrackers, I searched for Jerry. I passed the dips and ridges with its little dirt-bike jumps. I passed the creek where Jennifer Devries had fallen and broken both arms. I passed the pit where nude photos were once tacked up and hidden under a plywood roof. It was there, past the pits and beside the old, abandoned foundation that I found my cousin. He was stationary between an opening of trees, sitting cross legged like an Iroquois waiting for his prey. He had that blank look with his gleaming, brown eyes.

I sat beside him. No words entered my mind. I placed my hand on his shoulder. "Sorry," I whispered. I glanced down and laying in the dirt was one of Uncle Mike's long rifles.

The long black barrel poked through the leaves like a black snake.

I searched for something to say. "There are other schools out there. Saint Al's sucks."

"I can't ..." was all he said.

"We'll get you a tutor. My dad said he'd pay for it," I replied, feeling guilty for having lied about the teachers.

"It's all crap," was what he said.

"What are you doing out here?" I asked.

He lifted his finger and pointed it at his head, pretending to pull the trigger. My insides felt like a plate glass window bowing to a strong storm.

"You can't do that," I whispered.

I felt the phoniness of my existence swell like so many holiday movies and pop songs. I cycled through the weak emotions and found them lacking. I longed for an adult and responsible party to come to my aid. I wanted to run but Jerry looked down and closed his eyes like he was staring into a well. He was getting ready to do it.

"Wait," I said. "I have an idea. What if we go back and really mess with 'em?"

Jerry's eyes opened and he stared at me. His blond hair shifting ever so slightly. "You mean like we egg 'em?"

"Yeah," I replied. "Whatever you want. We got stuff at the house. Let 'em have it!"

A ribbon-shaped leaf floated past Jerry and shimmied to the ground. He seemed to be lost in thought. "If it doesn't work," he whispered, "I'm coming back here." He stood and placed the gun in the pit. "Let's go."

I'm not happy or proud of what we did. We raided my mother's fridge - eggs and pancake syrup. We ran to Saint Albert's, passing backyards and hiding in the grotto, stepping between the cars.

Mrs. Sim's car was easy to find. She had vanity plates that said, *TOOTSIE*. The gray Honda was a holy mess inside. We paused for just a moment before attacking. The eggs flew through the air, popping loudly against the windows. We knew they would ruin the paint. The syrup we dumped inside the locks and through the cracks in the hood. We imagined the sugar crystalizing the gears, locks, and belts. Jerry had a wild grin beneath his steely eyes as he jack-booted the side panel. He made a large dent that would forever be remembered.

After the vandalism, we returned home and ate left over Palermos. We sat in my room playing Atari for hours. I taught Jerry all my favorite games - Mike Tyson's Punch Out, Pitfall, DonkeyKong, and PacMan. Pac-Mac was Jerry's best game as he slammed the joystick back and forth gobbling up those shiny dots and turning on the Ghost Gang. One by one, Inky, Pinky, Blinky, and Clyde went down in a blaze of glory until they finally turned on him in the harder rounds. Slowly, Jerry relaxed. We laughed and joked about Mrs. Sims.

He handed me the joystick and said, "Your turn." He grabbed another slice of pizza and leaned back in the bean bag chair.

Later that night, my mom came in and said that Jerry would be returning home tomorrow. She said Aunty Judy was back from Denver and that she had a place for Jerry at Evergreen Park Academy in the industrial technology program. She said it with a high-pitch voice like this was really going to be the golden ticket in his life. Jerry was going to learn to become a mechanic.

It was all moving fairly well until the cops showed up at our door that Saturday. It seemed the janitor, whom we nicknamed, Good Frank, had seen two kids running out from behind the grotto. He recognized my purple Vikings jacket that my dad had brought home from a fishing trip. The police stood in our foyer telling my parents about security footage and Frank's testimony. Their handcuffs sparkled in the tiled entryway, and their radios chimed and dinged. They asked to speak to me and Jerry but aimed their questions at Jerry like he was their target. My face puckered, and I choked back my tears. I stepped forward.

"It was all *my* idea," I stated.

"Excuse me?" the officer asked. "Do you have something to tell us, young man?"

I told them that I hated Mrs. Sims for embarrassing my cousin. I told them she was always picking on me and my classmates. That I was tired of her being mean. There was some truth in what I said, which they took as convincing.

"What about the other one? Did anyone help you?" the officer asked, nodding at Jerry.

"No," I replied. "It was a one-man job."

"Okey-doke," the officer said, closing his notebook. "Thank you for your honesty. You did a lot of damage, and you'll have to suffer the consequences."

I received ten hours of community service, two-day suspension, and a bill for $1,300, but nothing that ended up on my permanent record. I worked as a lifeguard the following summer to pay back my parents.

A few days later, life was settling down and it was time for Jerry to leave. His mom arrived, and we said our goodbyes. He smirked as he shook my hand. He left with just his suitcase and backpack. I always wondered about the gun. A few weeks later, I ventured into the woods, back to the pit and hunted for that thing. I brought the gun home and placed it on the kitchen table. My mother cried out when she saw it. Then my father entered. He yelled at me and asked a hundred questions. I explained how I had found Jerry on the trails. My father looked deep into my eyes and said I did a good thing. He patted me on the back. I leaned the gun against the wall in his study next to his decommissioned World War II rifle where it sat for three months before being sold at a pawn shop.

When the dust finally settled and my suspension was over, I went back to Saint Albert's but it was never the same. Mrs. Sims' psychological hold was not the same after that. My friends looked at me different because of everything I had done. Shortly thereafter, I told my parents I wanted to transfer to a public school. They didn't ask questions. I switched the following week. The new class walls were a bright blue and red.

The public school had a big cafeteria and served warm chocolate chip cookies and chicken sandwiches. I became a starting pitcher on the boy's 16-inch softball team. I looked forward to Sunday dinners when Jerry visited. We played Pac-Man.

Eventually, Jerry stopped coming over for Sunday dinners. Work interfered and Reagan's term ended. Life gradually became more complicated. I attended UVM and studied in Australia. I grew up, and the Cubs never called. I became an assistant professor at the local community college and volunteered on the weekends at the shelter with my wife and son. Eventually, I learned about the church, the adoption, and the hardships that shaped Jerry's life. My dad died of cancer. Uncle Mike called Jerry just before he died and said he was proud of him.

My prodigal cousin, somewhat of a brother to me, was the only cousin I ever knew or loved.

Lynn's Thoughts …

Oh the wayward cousin. I believe we all have one of these somewhere. That one relative that fits in nowhere? And we're usually the ones left to make them feel better.

Gary gives a great account of what life was like when … when it was a little more simple. When Pac-Man mattered. A life with a mom that cooked, and a father that worked. And our responsibility was ensuring that our nuns remained happy.

The Prodigal Cousin gives us an idea as to how we are molded as a result of our parents. Doesn't matter if we were adopted or natural, we were still formed.

Teens are emotional. But they feel. How do we explain that as they grow their passions for life will settle? The future will be better. But at that awakening time, we honestly cannot see the forest for the trees.

The sweet revenge of the egg. Don't see it much anymore. Toilet paper was another favorite of the time. Don't see much of that anymore either. Maybe if we did, the kids of today would have something better to do. Better than rioting or … worse.

The Puddle

& The *Ghost*

Lady Beth

THE PUDDLE

Once upon a time, deep inside a magical forest lay a village where sprites and fairies roamed. The chief had two beautiful daughters, the youngest, Gwenivive, was a small, but tough, hardheaded sprite. Her older sibling, Willow, was reserved and quiet. Willow had already transformed and earned her wings after passing through the magical puddles. Raindrops were extremely valuable to this village. The magical drops were collected into four separate cauldrons – *courage, strength, compassion,* and *deception.* At the end of each season, the sprites tested their powers – who would be the next *chosen one.*

Gwenivive believed she was the black sheep of her family and village – a wild child always challenging their ancient ways. Growing up in the shadow of her elder sister, Gwenivive felt more of an outcast. Her friends were the forest animals, not the other sprites. Willow was close to her besties, Jade and Silke, who often taunted Gwenivive. Gwenivive looked up to her elder sister for inspiration until one day, something ignited, something deep inside her. The other fairies and sprites of the village knew Gwenivive was special in her own way.

However, instead of encouraging Gwenivive, their words only fueled her fire.

Gwenivive challenged her father's orders, growing impatient and spiteful. While her family slept, she crept out of their small tree hut and ran through the forest until she reached the cave. Gwenivive had seen the rituals before. She knew what to do.

Gwenivive used the small pail and scooped water from each cauldron, pouring them carefully into the Sacrificial Puddle. When the pool was filled, she took a deep breath and cannon balled in. Last season, a grown sprite that never transformed tried to force the process and made an unforgettable mistake. It cost them their life.

Once formed, the Sacrificial Puddle held mysterious powers. Gwenivive kept her eyes closed and held her breath. Her thoughts merged with the mysterious power that now challenged her strength and courage. The challenges were designed to test a sprite's mind and soul, to assess their mystical ability to grow and to face life's crossroads.

The power seeped deep into Gwenivive's most private memories. The small sprite had faced many battles. Battles she never told anyone except for her mammal friends. Gwenivive had kept a diary tucked secretly under her bed. A diary that her gom had gifted her.

The village never feared anything but one enemy – the *Ghost.* A paranormal form with extraordinary abilities. The *Ghost* would appear and disappear without notice. At times, the *Ghost* would take a sprite with it.

Gwenivive was the smallest sprite that ever lived. The village children often mocked and belittled her. They would push her out of their way, knocking her down more than once. Gwenivive felt invisible, a failure and saw no hope in her future.

Gwenivive acted out, starting fights. She was argumentative and confrontive. Her soul dripped, falling between the cracks of a darker self. She became moody and tempered. Foul language was frowned upon, but she took full advantage of each sour word. The sweet innocent sprite was no more, now consumed by her negative thoughts. Her hatred grew, only darkening her spirit.

The mysterious magic swirled around the darkness covering her soul. The power knew that if she stayed on her current path, Gwenivive would have no future. The mysterious magic dipped into her hidden memories and centered around a small flicker of happiness. An innocent sprite frolicking through the forest, helping injured animals. The mysterious magic understood why the mammals accepted Gwenivive as one of their own. She had a soft spot for furry critters. She bravely stood up for those whose voice was silenced. If only she would do the same for herself.

As the mysterious magic worked its way through her most sacred memories they hinged on a single event. They accepted the pain inside her teardrops. Would the magic decide against this outrage, and mark Gwenivive unfit, or would they reshape her actions?

Motion stirred inside the puddle. The waters quaked.

Day broke and Gwenivive's father found her bedroom empty. The town searched for the small sprite. They were worried that the *Ghost* had taken her. Willow found the hidden diary and the confession of Gwenivive's plan. A pit grew in Willow's stomach. She knew exactly where her little sister had gone.

Gwenivive's consciousness stirred. The rain poured, seeping through the ground, filtering through the cracks. A droplet hit the pool, and a gate opened to the other side. Gwenivive had already accepted her fate and was ready to surrender her soul to the underworld king. However, the angels had other plans. As her body awoke from a deep trance, Gwenivive broke through the mysterious power, fighting and floating up to the cave. The puddle spit her onto the cold, damp floor. She glanced up and smiled at the angels.

Gwenivive stepped outside and dropped to her knees. The rain pooled around her. She lowered her head, feeling defeated. The mud seeped through her fingers making her feel alive. She closed her eyes. The four challenges had completely broken her wild spirit. She was done. Done fighting with her father, her sister, the village, and more than anything else, herself.

She opened her eyes and stared at a pair of feet. Her father knelt and wrapped his arms around her. He spoke no words. Tears rolled down Gwenivive's cheeks.

A glow shown around Gwenivive, lifting her higher into the rain. Her father stepped back. No other sprite was ever affected this way. No sprite ever glowed. As she floated higher into the trees, an electrifying energy shot through Gwenivive, and she screamed. The force lowered her, and she planted her feet firmly back on the ground. She had been renewed. In order to fulfill her duties, she would need to stay true to herself and her village. When the time was right, she would return to the mysterious puddle and finish the transformation. Until then, Gwenivive needed to grow and mature.

THE GHOST

It was springtime in the magical forest, and Gwenivive awoke with excitement. She secretly crept to her gom's cabin eager to start her summer. Every summer the chief sent his daughters to stay with his mother, Evalyn. Evalyn played a special role within the village. Her farm collected morning dew, which was used in the village. This morning was Gwenivive's first visit without her sister. She felt free without Willow's constant glare.

Evalyn's farm was placed at the far end of the forest just before the creek. The creek was off limits to the fairy folk. The territory belonged to another family in another reality. As Gwenivive crept in, Evalyn shut her eyes and listened for the floorboards to creek. She sprung up, scooping Gwenivive into her arm. The little sprite made a loud squeak as she giggled. They made their way to the kitchenette, and her gom conjured up a tasty breakfast. The hotcakes were stacked as tall as Gwenivive. With a whisk of her gom's hand, the mess disappeared. The day's work was to begin. Pails in hand, they collected the dewdrops. Placing each pail next to a leaf, tugging it downward, the dewdrop rolled effortlessly into the pail. Once the pail was filled, the drops were deposited into the big vase. The vase was connected to several pipes, allowing droplets to flow to the village.

They finished their chores just before lunch. Gwenivive's stomach growled and her gom entered the cabin to make lunch. Gwenivive wandered across the fields and entered an open meadow. Two bunnies were playing in the tall grass. Gwenivive took a step, and a blur crossed her vision. A shiver ran up her spine. A trail of frost now ran across the ground in front of her. She reached down, but the glittering had disappeared. She glanced over to where the bunnies were playing but they were gone too. The leaves rustled and danced through the air. Gwenivive felt herself drawn toward them. She stood at the edge of the forest, staring at the forbidden creek.

How did I get here?

A dark form faded in before her. She gasped, but no sound escaped. The dark form looked elegant and mysterious. Gwenivive's gom called out for her. The floating mist disappeared and Gwenivive ran to the cabin. Evalyn was standing on the porch, hand on hips, shaking her head.

"My child, where did you run off to?"

"To the meadow," Gwenivive replied.

Evalyn seemed puzzled. The seventy-three years she lived on the farm, Evalyn knew nothing of a meadow. "Silly, child, I have no meadow on this farm."

"Yes, you do," Gwenivive stated. "At the edge of the forest."

After lunch, Evalyn and Gwenivive would go find this mysterious meadow. Gwenivive failed to mention the creature that had floated over the creek. She was afraid she would get spoken to. Over lunch, they shared stories of the previous season's events. Gwenivive mentioned that her sister had completed her Jollity. The Jollity was a big event for the sprites coming of age. During the rise of the blue moon, the sprites would test themselves in the puddle in order to transform into fairies.

"Do you know why we collect the morning dew, my child?" Evalyn asked.

Gwenivive shook her head.

"It's the key to our survival," Evalyn replied. "Each drop holds magical powers."

The two strolled through the farm searching for the mysterious meadow. Evalyn showed Gwenivive the important details about the land. She hadn't quite understood why her gom was telling her all this. As they walked, Gwenivive thought she might be crazy for they covered the entire farm and found no meadow.

As dusk approached, they came across an overturned ladybug. Gwenivive knelt to help it back on its feet when she felt that same cold shiver run up her back. She stood and spun around, pointing at the mysterious meadow.

"See! she exclaimed.

"My child," Evalyn said, "what are you seeing?"

Gwenivive looked down and frowned. "I was looking at that creature who visited me."

Evalyn's face paled and her hands trembled. "It's not safe out here."

"Gom, you're scaring me. What's wrong?"

Evalyn did not respond. Instead, she scooped up Gwenivive and darted for the cabin. Before they could reach the safety of the door, Evalyn froze. They were now standing in front of the creek.

"Run, child," Evalyn whispered. "Run and don't look back!"

Gwenivive did not want to leave her beloved gom.

Evalyn gave Gwenivive a slight push and stated, "Go! Go now!"

Gwenivive stumbled as she ran. She was afraid to leave her gom and ducked behind an old toadstool. Peaking our, she watched as the mysterious creature materialized in front of her precious gom.

"Please, Ghost," Evalyn said, "it is too soon. My family needs me.

The Ghost chuckled and replied, "I have given you a season. You should be ready now."

Evalyn fell to her knees, begging for forgiveness, begging for more time.

A skeletal hand appeared from the dark cloud, reaching out for Evalyn's hand. "Don't make this any harder than it needs to be."

"No!" Gwenivive yelled out, standing up.

The Ghost glanced up, and Evalyn nodded at Gwenivive. A slight stir of static stung the air. The two vanished. Now, a dusted layer of frost covered Evalyn's footprints. A black shadow seeped across the meadow, surrounding Gwenivive's soul. An icy gust of wind swarmed, knocking Gwenivive to the ground.

From inside a hollow log, Slinky, a kit, watched. With the darkness now gone, she scampered over to Gwenivive and sniffed.

"She smells funny," Slinky whispered.

She carefully picked up the little sprite and darted into the safety of the hollow log. Slinky's family of skunks were the forest's defenders.

"What do you have now?" Slinky's mother, Mildred, asked. She looked furious.

Their home was under an old oak tree just inside a quaint den. Fairy folk never crossed paths with the defenders. Each stayed to their own. Slinky set the little sprite inside her nook and smiled. She then described what she had witnessed to her mother.

"I'm sorry I left my post, Mother," Slinky said. "But I had to!"

Mildred shook her head.

They agreed that the little sprite would stay with them for a while.

Gwenivive soon woke and her mind spun with the lingering aroma of pine. Her world had been flipped upside down. In a single day, her happiness was ripped away. The one person who cared and loved her was now gone. The Ghost's words rang through her ears, *'You had a season.'* Gwenivive felt confused. Why hadn't her gom mentioned this before? Is this why she was explaining the farm to her? Who would take on the responsibility now? The fairies' world was doomed.

Slinky handed Gwenivive a mug of hot cocoa.

"Thank you," Gwenivive whispered.

Four hot cocoas later, Gwenivive felt a little more comfortable. Mildred discussed with Gwenivive the ways of the farm, and the responsibilities that went along with it. They discussed setting up a plan. Once it was set, Mildred knew it would be time for a new family tradition.

The first full moon was out and shining. Food was stacked tall in various crates. The fire crackled in the silent air. As other families arrived, the festival roared to life. By the end of the evening, Slinky and Gwenivive were exhausted and fell asleep in Slinky's nook.

At first light the crickets chirped. It was time to start the morning's work. Gwenivive and Slinky made their way to the farm where they grabbed the pails and collected the morning dew. When she slung the last pail into the vase, Gwenivive smiled. The day's work was finished. A tear formed in the corner of Gwenivive's eyes. She held back her emotions for she had to be strong. Day after day, the two collected the morning dew. In the afternoon, they frolicked through the forest.

It was the last day of the season, and the chief had arrived. It was time for the sprites' Jollity. The chief approached the cabin, but he saw or heard no one. He glanced over at the forest and listened to his daughter's giggle. He wondered where his mother was for she was no where to be seen.

Gwenivive squeaked and ran to her father. They hugged. She then took her father's hand, and they sat on a nearby log. Gwenivive explained everything that had happened. The chief nodded and hugged his daughter.

"Daughter, I am proud of you."

Gwenivive was glad to have a new friend in Slinky. But the season had ended. As time approached to leave for home, Gwenivive knew the farm would be in safe hands. Things were about to change. The struggle was real, but Gwenivive was a fighter and would not back down. After one last hug, Gwenivive waved farewell to her new friends. She had made a promise to Slinky, she would return next season.

Lynn's Thoughts …

Perhaps fairytales will never go out of fashion. The meaning of the name, Gwenivive, is *tribe woman*, which fits in this story. And of course, self-sacrifice, the gom (grandmother) gave up her life to the Ghost to save her granddaughter. And of course, the granddaughter steps up to replace her grandmother. Thus Gwenivive becomes the woman of her tribe. Fits …

Our author, Lady Beth, gives us a glimpse of the old through her written voice. Old English slips through from time to time, which takes us back to another time and place. The visual description is excellent, and I see green everywhere with fairies and sprites of various colors. Even the Sacrificial Puddle seemed wise and tolerant in this story.

An enjoyable read …

The Undead Friendzone

Tyler Tarter

Well, it happened. The thing the world was terrified would happen, happened. And I'm still alive. I'm not sure if I should be worried, but my job said to pretend like nothing happened. Despite all of this, I felt like I had to record my story for posterity.

My name ... Zac McGee, and I was an IT Manager for a local office of the Bureau of Synthetic Stenography. If I was being honest, I would have to admit that I had no idea what we actually did in that office. Living and working in our small valley made it easy to fall into a routine that could never be broken, and now I was stuck in one of the worst ruts of my life.

It all started with me rolling out of bed with a blaring alarm. I couldn't help but feel as if today would be just another of the many bland days that was occupying my life. After a quick shower, I threw on the newest version of my usual, office outfits. As the next alarm blared, I grabbed my homemade parfait before running out the door, late as usual.

Without another thought, I pulled out of the driveway with my newest audiobook playing in the background. I tried not to let my thoughts drift as I drove into the graying fog and darkening skies that surrounded me. I turned up the heat not wanting to admit that something might be bothering me.

When I stopped at an intersection, I couldn't help but look for what was pushing me to the edge. Something was moving inside the distant mist, but the familiar sound of old school horror music broke my attention. Laughing that it was just my nerves, I voiced my thoughts to break the tension.

"Why did Alex have to talk me into listening to this? She knows I hate horror stories. If I keep listening, I'm bound to jump at something."

I drove in silence, feeling weird talking to the darkening fog. I rolled to a stop and watched for the usual heavy traffic ripping back and forth. But nothing. The light turned green and I turned left, continuing into the mist, wondering if I had my days mixed up. Was I about to walk into the office on a Saturday?

I made my way into the building, watching the fog swirl as it faded into a thinner haze. The morning light cutting through revealed only abandoned streets. Most of the office was huddled together in the bullpen, speaking in hushed tones. I wove through the desks as Alex intercepted me – her usual jovial face wrinkled as she ran her hands through her hair.

"About time. Chris needs to talk to us. It's pretty bad out there."

Confusion grew, the tension palpable. Inside a spartan office, three other department heads sat around a small conference table, talking quietly. Taking a seat next to Alex, I leaned back and pushed the door closed.

Chris jumped right in, his voice somber and quiet, making me focus on every word. "I'm sure you've heard the news, but it's worse than what they're saying. We've been instructed to maintain a presence to keep up public perception. We'll be sending most of the staff home to work. Call your teams and let them know. But we do need volunteers from each department to continue coming in. It's been confirmed, once someone turns, it's over ... fatal. Tell your people to prepare."

I leaned over to Alex, speaking softly, "What am I missing? Turns?" I regretted the question.

A stunned look shot across her heart, shaped face. Her surprise shifted to a mild annoyance mixed with a little disappointment. "Of course, you didn't hear. What was it this time, researching mythical languages or maybe fifteenth century kings of Andorra?"

I grabbed my chest as if shot, flopping on the table to finish the charade. Groaning, Alex shook my shoulder until I smirked. "You know I'm writing a sci-fi story. I fell down the warp bubbles versus Einstein-Rosen Bridge theories for space travel. I'll bet you spent the weekend playing that new game you've been talking about. Are you going to tell me what happened or not?"

Alex sighed. "I know you watched my stream, so you know exactly how I spent my weekend. I was playing *Serial Killer Brawl*, but that's not the point. You had to have heard about Mors Eclampsia, it's all anyone can talk about."

I tried to remember where I had heard that name. Cutting back to the news, it took a few seconds to remember the talking heads that'd been the background noise of my last visit to my parents. "The virus that's running around somewhere in East Africa? What does that have to do with us?"

Despite seeing her face, I knew her eyes were rolling. "It started in the lower Nile Valley on Wednesday. By Friday, it was in Europe and Asia. By Saturday, it arrived on both coasts of the U.S. Lockdown orders haven't been given yet, but this must mean they're close."

The weight of the situation hit me like a freight train. Shaking my head, I stood and stared into my best friend's eyes. "I had no idea it was this bad."

She gave me an unexpected hug, letting me feel her words against my chest as much as hear them. "It's bad ... I mean really bad," she whispered. "Basically, the virus turns people into monsters ... living zombies. The scientists are saying that once infected, you're dead. I'm not sure how we're going to keep this office going if it gets any worse."

I held tightly to the women that anchored my life despite her desires to remain friends. "You and I are in this together," I said. "No matter what happens, I'm here. Let's tell our teams the news."

Picking up my phone as it buzzed and trumpeted on my nightstand, I tried to shake off the sleep that held my mind prisoner. With the phone near my eyes, I tried to see what had woken me from my dreams. Instead of the usual screen that displayed when most called, Alex's face appeared. Her giant, white headphones on her head, and her calico cat sitting on her lap, looking bored.

With a swipe of my thumb, I answered, mostly asleep. "Why are you calling before the sun's up?"

The fear in her whispered voice sent chills down my spine. "Zac! Something's happening. Screams and a few gunshots. Can you come get me?"

I bolted out of bed and ran to the safe that sat in the corner of my room. I took an inventory of the weapons I had collected over the years. "It'll take me about twenty minutes. Grab what you can. Block the door until I get there?"

"Okay ... okay ... I can use the table to do that. Will you call when you're close?"

"Of course, be there soon."

I used a wet rag to wipe away the night's sweat. I threw on pants and a t-shirt, intentionally picking dark colors to make me harder to spot. After pulling on my old, black, combat boots, I strapped on my shoulder, ankle, and waist holsters, filling each with a 9mm pistol and two spare clips. I added five knives and three combat tomahawks of various sizes. Taking a deep breath, I pulled on my thin jacket for the predawn summer morning and grabbed a shotgun and rifle. I stepped out the front door and made my way to my jeep.

Just like the day before, the valley was filled with fog, making it impossible to see more than a few yards in front of me. My headlights cut a small hole in the wall of gray, showing just enough to keep me safe. For most of the drive, I didn't see much. The city had obviously locked down, and by now, no one dared set foot outside.

When I reached Alex's complex, the place was active and none of it good. Inside the gated courtyard in the center of her u-shaped building was a small group of what once had been humans. They were now milling around inside a jerky, mindless swarm. Knowing I couldn't beat those numbers, I drove to the parking garage, using the guest card that Alex had given me. I slowly inched up to the parking level that would enter onto the third floor.

I parked and with a deep breath tapped the access card against the reader, letting my rifle lead the way as I slipped through to the hallway. Moving slow, I worked my way down the long corridor, searching for the stairs. I pushed the stairwell open and glanced down to see two zombie-like beings stumbling, unable to open the small safety gate. To avoid drawing attention, I resisted the urge to shoot.

A small squeak was the only sound as the hallway door to the fourth floor swung open. Using the outer wall to navigate, I worked my way past six doors until I stood in front of the one that was painted to look like a stormtrooper's helmet. Pulling out my phone, I sent a text.

The door across the hall opened.

I whipped up my rifle, finding a woman standing with two small children at her side, terror in their eyes. Lowering the weapon, I held a finger to my lips. "If you want to leave, I can take you to the garage. Do you have some place to go?"

She nodded.

"Grab your things. We leave in two minutes. I wish I could give you more time, but I can't."

I stepped into Alex's apartment. The door closed and I relaxed, taking Alex into my arms. Her fear bled, shaking through her body.

"You're okay now," I whispered. "I'm here. We're taking your neighbor out with us. Are you ready?"

She grabbed her backpack and cat carrier.

"Here, take this. Use only if you must."

Her eyes grew wide as she stared at the gun. I kissed her softly on the forehead before knocking on the neighbor's door. It opened and the mother and two children frowned at me.

I knelt in front of the boy and his sister. "We're going to play a game. I want to see who can be the quietest. Can you do that?"

The boy nodded.

"We're going to the third floor of the garage," I whispered to the mother. "I'll get you safely to your car and follow you out. I didn't run into any issues on my way in, but I can't guarantee anything on the way out. What floor is your car on?"

Not saying a word, she held up three fingers before glancing back at Alex who was quietly locking her door.

"Stay behind us and alert for anything that moves."

With my rifle pointed down the hallway, we inched our way out. More worried about speed than sound, I kept my eyes and ears open. Stepping through the stairway door, I paused, careful not to make any sound on the metal grates. Standing on the third-floor landing, a soft thump from above caused me to look up. The little girl had dragged one of her bags down the stairs. I shook my head and glared at the mother.

Two zombies stepped up from the second floor, disfigured and searching for prey.

It took two rounds to the head to drop them, but the noise had called attention to the others. The rattle of zombies trying to climb the bottom gate made me pause. I leaned over the railing and pulled the trigger. A limp body fell over the railing, and I waited for the harsh thump on the floor below before calling the others to follow.

I opened the garage door and stepped onto the wide walkway. I turned to the mother and Alex, speaking softly, "My jeep is over there. Alex'll get into my jeep, and I'll escort you to your car. Once you're in, don't use your lights. We should be okay if we hurry." Handing Alex my keys, I swiveled my rifle from side to side. No threats. "I want you outta here if anything goes wrong. Make a quick escape if you have to. I'll do what I can to find you later. But if I go down, you leave."

She reached up and grabbed my jacket, pulling me into a soft but strong kiss. "I can't lose you. Don't make me choose."

"I love you too. But if we're going to live, we need to do this now. Stay close behind me in the jeep."

We walked cautiously down the sloped floor to the blue Toyota sitting quietly in the shadows. Chittering and scraping from the main floor sent chills all through me. The woman was hurrying to strap her children into their seats when a loud hiss echoed out, followed by padded footsteps. I whipped around as a zombie pushed me to the ground. Its jaws snapped, and I used my rifle to hold it back.

The woman's car squealed as she backed out of the space. The deformed being spread its legs, pushing more weight on my rifle.

A crack of a pistol broke, and an explosion of greenish, red blood splattered the car beside me. I pushed off the limp body, rolling away from the gore. With my rifle up and pointing down the winding path, I ran up to the jeep where Alex was still pointing the pistol. I lowered it and smiled.

"You did good. You drive, I'll shoot. Stop for nothing until we're outside the city."

We climbed into the jeep, and I rested my hand on her leg for a just moment before I felt the jerk and us rolling forward. Spotting the flashes of movement below, I spoke just loud enough for her to hear over the rising chaos of cars and zombies.

"Time to move, we can't leave that woman and her kids alone."

Alex veered around the corner, giving me my first clean shot at the zombies as they poured through the doorway that led from the courtyard. Hanging out the window, I raked the deadly creatures with bullets as they stepped through. A barrier of bodies was now slowing the rest of the horde. Pivoting as we rounded the last corner, I cleared off the remaining zombies that were trying to attack the woman's car. She plowed through the exit and into the vacant street.

Switching out my empty rifle for the shotgun, I sent a few blasts into the collapsing masses before rolling up the window. After a deep breath, I placed my hand back on Alex's leg.

"Maybe the military will control this before it gets any worse," I whispered.

I tried to keep track of the zombies that were following us. When we reached the highway, I relaxed. I dialed the emergency number that we'd been given the day before.

The automated female voice answered, and I replied, "A large infection is spreading from Seventy-Four South to Fifty East. Large response needed to contain the incident. Several shots fired by fleeing parties, casualties, and trapped people on site."

After receiving confirmation, I hung up and slumped deeper into my seat. I closed my eyes as I tried to shut off the soldier that was wakening inside me. A soft sniffle broke my focus, pulling me back into the car. It only took my logical mind a moment to understand. Reaching over, I wiped the tears from her cheeks.

"Everything'll be fine. We're together, and I'll never let anything happen to you. Whatever is ahead of us, we'll do it together."

She smiled as she kept her focus on the road. Her voice, soft despite the pattering rain that had started during our escape. "We've been a team for a while, but it took zombies to make us appreciate what we have. Hopefully we'll push through this. But despite this rain, I'm sure we will."

I nodded.

Lynn's Thoughts …

Zombies … our next pandemic? Or maybe the zombie-ant fungus (ophiocordyceps unilateralis). I read a novel once about this fungus that infected humans. The fungus takes over the brain and controls the host. At the end of the lifecycle, the host then grows this *thing* from its body that will eventually burst, creating more spores to attack more hosts. It's quite gruesome.

Tyler definitely gives a realistic approach to a modern day occurrence if such a pandemic should happen. Some people will know what is happening and some will not, having the situation bloom around them, so to speak.

The story, a mixture of apocalyptic-destruction and love meets somewhere in the middle, where the hero can ride up on his white horse (jeep) and save the day.

I enjoyed this story mostly because the man does become the hero and saves the woman he loves and another family. In today's society, many are claiming that we can do without men, that we can do it alone. I will argue to differ. Relationships are more than he's in charge or she's in charge. Marriage becomes a team, two people who love and work together to meet their common goals. Exactly what Tyler says at the end. Team work …

Ticket to Abbeville

Kristine K. McCraw

Sleeping on a mattress with a soft pillow and blanket is something I'll never take for granted again. I don't know how anyone can sleep in jail. The cell is nothing but concrete. No pillows or blankets. A heartless place that robs people of their humanity.

I was released in the morning and took an Uber home. After a shower, I slumped into my bed – swollen eyes, aching body, bruised wrists, and feeling broken to the core. I woke to a noon sun shining through my window. The nightmare I just lived came rushing back as I wiped the sleep from my eyes.

Another rant, another threat, another tirade of insults, and finally I had called the police on Joey. I wanted them to make him leave, but when they knocked on the door, Joey forced me to a kitchen chair.

"I'll handle this," he said in his usual dominant manner.

He was on the sidewalk, talking with the police. I cracked open the door and heard the lies.

"I tried to calm her down, but she hit me, officer." He wasn't trying to get the police to leave. He was making me to be the bad one.

I stepped outside and the officers' eyes met mine.

"Please wait inside the apartment," one of the officers ordered.

"I'm not drunk!" My anger boiled and desperation drove me to kick Joey. My last resort was to push this man out of my home, but the officers didn't see it that way. I was placed under arrest for assault. The handcuffs hit my wrist, and as the cold metal clapped against my bones, I fought to break free, but an arrest cannot be undone. Joey spent the night in my bed while I was carted off to jail.

I crawled out of bed to an apartment that was a complete mess. The pile of dishes I washed first, and it somehow gave me a moments relief. His clothes scattered across the floor I shoved into a garbage bag. I sifted through a hefty pile of mail and found an envelope labeled *Final Notice*. I hadn't paid the rent in maybe two, three, or even four months. I desperately had hoped Mr. Randall would give me more time to catch up, but the letter in the envelope was indeed an eviction notice. I had to think of what to do, but my anxiety sent my thoughts pinging in all directions.

I stepped outside. The worn lounge chair on the patio gave me a quiet place to collect my thoughts. I closed my eyes and took a deep, slow breath, just like Dr. Sparrow had taught me. The warmth of the afternoon sun caressed my face, and my mind sent me back to my childhood where Hannah took us on picnic lunches. She was big on picnics during the summer months. Just the two of us sitting on a blanket while the rest of my foster siblings played manhunt in the forest. She brought out the plates and the food but stole a moment before calling in the crew. She leaned on her hands and stared up at the sun, soaking in the rays. Try it, Jessica, she urged. I did. I leaned on my hands and tilted my head. From where I sat, the trees blocked the sun. Hannah pulled me closer, and I leaned back again. I sat motionless, allowing the warmth to cover my face. My heart warmed. I thought this was better than playing, and I liked having Hannah all to myself. That day, I knew she loved me as I opened my eyes to the swaying birch branches. If only I had never left Hannah's and Jack's.

The few minutes on the porch calmed me, but I hadn't yet thought of a plan. Inside the apartment, I checked my phone. The time startled me. Joey would return soon, and I didn't want to see him. Last night's tirade began when I asked him to move out. My reasons were numbered in a neatly typed letter – just like an eviction notice. It was never good when I spoke my mind. The letter made him angry as would the garbage bag stuffed with his things. I couldn't call the police again. Since he was my boyfriend, he had a right to stay, as I learned last night. He was the perpetrator, yet the law protected him, and I suppose that's why I took matters into my own hands when I tried to kick him out. I couldn't do that again. My five-foot-four height was miniature compared to his six-foot frame and muscular body. I was left with two choices – stay in the apartment where I would be evicted in two weeks with an abuser or escape. I chose to escape.

Escaping was like an old friend. By the time I was eight, I had escaped with my mother twelve times. She was always running from her demons. I escaped from Hannah's and Jack's two years ago. Now, I was escaping from Joey, but I had to move quickly.

I combed my hair and touched up my makeup, hoping to cover the dark circles and weariness under my eyes. I pulled the rose luggage from the closet and stuffed them with clothes. I had to press the flap with my knee to zip it. I filled the strapped bag with makeup and shoes, and slung it over my shoulder, pulling the larger case behind me. My old car had just enough gas to make it to the bus station, where I would abandon it. I was never coming back. Since moving to this town, life had become impossible, and last night's episode was the last.

The bus station was claustrophobic – dirty and smelled like un-showered bodies. I bought a ticket, sat in a chair or paced the floor. My escape took a long time to wait.

I thought about what I was leaving behind – nothing but hardships. I came to this town to be with my mother. After handing me over to the system, my mother moved here to recover. She had to attend ninety days of rehab, counseling, and take a parenting class to get me back. But my mother left rehab after the second week. When I graduated high school, I left Hannah's and Jack's to live with my mother. I wanted to save her, and I thought that if I loved her enough, she would recover. And maybe she could love me back.

At first, she progressed, but a relapse took her life. Never did I hear what I wanted to hear before she died – those three little words. At the morgue and before the medical examiner covered her, I whispered,

"I love you, Mom." Hannah wanted me to return with them, but I couldn't because Joey had me convinced that he loved me.

At the bus station, my stomach growled. In the rush to leave, I had forgotten to eat. I had also forgotten to bring food. I last ate just before I left the letter for Joey on the table. The vending machine held candy bars, chips, and drinks, which were not the healthiest of food but would stave off my hunger. Joey always had change lying around, and I gathered every coin before I left. He at least bought me snacks for the eight-hour ride. An announcement stated to load the bus. I gathered my things and hobbled to the ramp, where I had left my roller suitcase to be packed underneath. With my carry-on bag slung over my shoulder and my over-stuffed purse swinging off the other, I stepped to the top of the stairs and waited for my ticket to be collected.

"Ticket to Abbeville, please." The driver reached out his hand.

I stiffened at the sound of Abbeville. That was where Hannah and Jack lived.

"I'm not going to Abbeville," I said. "I need the bus for Myrtle Beach." In Myrtle Beach, the hotels were cheap in the offseason, and I was sure to land a job within a day or two.

"The bus to Myrtle Beach left this afternoon. There isn't another for three days. Are you going or not, miss?" His bark told me I had better decide and fast but still, I was convinced that Myrtle Beach was my destination.

"Then why does my ticket say Myrtle Beach?" I held the ticket to my face. Instead of Myrtle Beach, Abbeville was typed next to the word – arrival. I felt as stupid as I did landing in jail for kicking Joey.

"What's it gonna be?" His voice filled the bus as if he was speaking through a megaphone.

"C'mon, lady," someone yelled.

The seats shifted and voices echoed behind me.

The driver rolled his eyes. My face flushed. I felt flustered and couldn't remember exactly what had happened at the ticket counter. I proceeded to a seat to save myself more embarrassment. I would figure it out later.

Abbeville?

I could have sworn I had said Myrtle Beach – too late now. Returning to the apartment where Joey was probably smoking pot and angry as hell was definitely out of the question. I could get to Abbeville and maybe see Hannah and Jack before I left for some place else. Hannah always told me I was welcome but going back to live would be out of the question. They had urged me to stay after high school and attend the local community college. They weren't my parents and had no obligation once I turned eighteen. But, in reality, I wanted to save my mother. When she came to be with me for the funeral, Hannah was sympathetic and caring. I was just too guarded to show emotions. Instead, I embellished my life as if I were dressing up a dull pair of shoes with rhinestones.

"My job is great, and I met someone who treats me wonderful. I'm so happy."

I had lied. Hannah's reaction told me that she knew better, but she gave me the space to believe what I needed to believe.

Right on time, the bus lurched forward and rolled out of the parking lot toward the highway. Rain sprinkled down the windows, and the moon hid behind the clouds. The bus sped with its lights beaming through a wall of darkness. Only a few cars were traveling at this late hour, and we would likely arrive on time in Abbeville. In the meantime, I needed to sleep. Thoughts of Joey were as gone as every post we passed, but the thoughts of my mother lingered. As much as I wanted to tuck her away, I couldn't.

I bunched up my jacket for a makeshift pillow and nested into the most comfortable position I could. The rhythm of the motor was somewhat relaxing until the tiny raindrops turned into pellets. The bus bobbed and swayed with every roar of the wind. I felt nauseous and uncomfortable. I rubbed my hand in circles on my stomach, as I always did when I felt sick. The first time was when I entered foster care. Hannah had rubbed my belly for me.

"Why are you doing that?" I asked.

"It'll calm your stomach, Jess."

That was the first time she had called me Jess. My stomachache disappeared. No one had ever rubbed my belly before, and I felt cared for. When I was with my mother, I was the one comforting her when she was sick, and she was often sick.

I drifted off to sleep and woke to a drizzling rain. I checked my phone. A text from Joey.

How was jail LOL where the hell are you stupid ...

Before I read the last word, I deleted the message and blocked him. Two years of experiencing his insults were enough. He would just upset me and last night my anger had me arrested. I needed nothing to do with Joey, and I was proud for making that decision.

I know now I shouldn't have had anything to do with my mother, either. I stopped my life to save hers, and it only brought me grief. She had opened credit cards in my name and stole money from me to support her drug habit. She brought unsavory and scary men home after her drinking binges. After my mother died, I thought Joey was my savior. I thought he loved me, but he didn't. Joey doesn't love anyone but himself – maybe my mother was like Joey in that way.

By now, it was one in the morning, and the bus was moving fast. I stared out the window. There wasn't much I could see but a dark cloud filling the sky and outlining the landscape. I reached into my purse for a Snickers Bar and a Diet Coke, and when I was just about to tear it open, the emergency signal sounded on my phone. No passenger was beside me, but I heard the other phones blaring out the same warning – flashes of light turning on and off.

"Mommy, what's all the noise?" a young girl asked from behind. "I'm scared."

I turned to the voice and watched as the mother roped her arm around her little girl.

The driver made an announcement, "Don't worry folks, that emergency is for Morrisville County, fifty miles away. We'll be making a stop in about forty minutes."

But five minutes later, the wind gusted, and the rain pummeled the roof of the bus. The worried girl cried. I peeked over the seat, and she was burrowing her face into her mother's chest. The little girl braids reminded me of when Hannah would braid my hair. She spent half an hour weaving the strands in and out while my head was pulled in different directions. When she was finished, she handed me a mirror. My scraggly brown strands were off my face in a neat weave. It was much different than the mess my hair was when I lived with my mother. Hannah gave me a special conditioner, and it made my dry wispy hair silky and smooth.

"It really brings out your eyes," Hannah had said.

I looked again. My blue eyes shined like sea glass. I held back a smile with a mighty effort and told Hannah I hated it. Then, I ran to the bathroom and cut off the braids. After Hannah saw me with short, uneven, and choppy hair, she closed herself in her bedroom with Jack. Jack always had a way of soothing things over with us. Later that evening, we were all watching a movie in the den. Hannah was on the end of the couch crocheting. Jack sauntered into the room and handed me a Red Sox baseball cap. He told me it went perfect with my haircut. Hannah pulled her mouth into a soft smile as she stayed fixed on her work. When I looked at Sabrina and Charlene, I noticed their French braids, and here I sat with a baseball cap like Brendan. Sabrina and Charlene laughed, but Hannah scolded them for making fun. It was then I wished I had kept the braids.

Forty minutes after the emergency call, we stopped for a break.

"Thirty minutes," the driver belted out. "Be back on the bus so you're not left behind." This bus driver was sticking to a tight schedule.

The truck stop was like a ghost town. The wind swirled dried leaves and bits of trash through the parking lot. I noticed the moon peeking out between the fast-moving clouds. I trotted to the building. I visited the restroom then stood outside, keeping a close eye on the bus. The building and parking lot were well-lit, but beyond the perimeters, the darkness was thick. I peered into the nothingness, and it felt like my life meant nothing. I had no one to call a best friend, my mother was gone, and I had left the only family that ever loved me. I felt stupid for believing that Joey wanted me. I was naïve to think I could save my mother. As much as I didn't like that bus driver, I needed him to take me home. *Home.* I hadn't used that word for Hannah and Jack's in a long time.

"Five minutes," the bus driver yelled.

People started loading on the bus. When I reached the top of the steps, the driver asked sarcastically, "Still going to Abbeville?"

"Yes, sir. Going to Abbeville," I replied, rolling my eyes.

The bus ventured on, and I felt like a stretched rubber band. I desperately wanted a hot meal and a good night's sleep. But for now, it was chips, water, and this bus seat.

I texted Hannah.

'Hannah, I'm on my way to Abbeville for a visit. Can you pick me up from the bus stop? My bus comes in at 6:18 AM. Sorry for the last-minute notice.' I added a smiley face emoji.

Hannah probably wouldn't see my message 'till she woke up. She was usually up at six but always needed at least three cups of coffee before she could function. I'd probably have to wait before she could pick me up.

When I was in junior high, Hannah encouraged me to become involved.

"You have much to offer," she always told me.

I tried student council to get her off my back about being involved, but it was difficult with the kids on the student council in Abbeville High School. No one had an addict mother who left them in foster care. Those kids looked like their parents and siblings, and most had only one last name. Between Hannah and Jack, Sabrina, Charlene, Brendan, and me, we had five last names, and neither of us resembled each other. One day when she came to pick me up, I wasn't at school because I had quit. I left with a friend and tried pot for the first time. Hannah was mad, and again, Jack helped to smooth things over. This time, he made sure I found a job as a cashier in the Food Market.

I knew it was never easy for Hannah. She loved me as her own, but I had already built walls around me. I kept my heart as cold and hard as that bench in jail. She tried to hide it, but I always noticed a particular frustration that she held with Sabrina, Charlene, or Brendan. I was angry with my mom, angry with my life. My mom was supposed to love me, so why would I let Hannah or Jack love me? The things that rob us of our ability to love. For my mother, it was the drugs, and for me, it was my hardened heart. Suddenly, my eyes were holding back a flood. Then the threshold broke, and the crying was unstoppable. Luckily, I still had a seat to myself.

When I woke, the bus was pulling into Abbeville Station on time. I had three solid hours of sleep after the truck stop. I didn't hear the rain or feel the bus bump up and down or sway in the wind. I checked my phone. No response from Hannah. People were stepping off the bus. I stood and stretched before grabbing my belongings. After walking inside the station, I texted Jack. Sabrina had moved out after college. Charlene was probably away at college. And Brendan probably had reunited with his father. As far as I knew, only Hannah and Jack were in the house. Hannah and Jack still owned a health food store in downtown Abbeville, and it wasn't open this early. One of them should be able to pick me up – I hoped.

I stood in the center as others rushed around in different directions. The dark night had drifted into a bright morning, and for the first time in a long time, I felt lighter. I could escape all I wanted, but if I didn't let go of the past, it would rob me of what I was missing.

I walked outside to enjoy the fresh air and sunshine. A bench next to the door beckoned me. I rolled my large suitcase and sat. I pulled out my phone, snapped a picture of the beautiful morning, and checked the photo. Something I had captured felt familiar and secure. I looked closer and stared at a woman with blonde cropped hair. Her chin tilting toward the sun. Her fair skin and cherry lips glowed under the morning rays. There was a man behind her looking at the bus station. His thin physique and light windswept hair reminded me of Jack. I glanced up from my phone and smiled. They were standing only a few feet away.

"Hannah! Jack!"

Hannah smiled and Jack held his usual everything-was-peachy grin.

"Jess. You made it!" Hannah looked into my eyes, and for the first time, I clasped my arms around her. She held onto me, and I held onto her. Without a thought of my mother, I let myself *feel* Hannah's love. Jack took my suitcase, and the three of us walked side by side to their car.

Hannah and Jack took me home. My bedroom was still the same as when I had left – rose-colored walls, a frilly white lamp, and a pink and white plaid, bed cover topped with fluffy pillows. That night, I slept under warm blankets, the best night's sleep I ever had.

I am still deciding where I will escape to next. But for now, I'm staying home, helping Hannah and Jack in their store while I attend college. They offered to help me through my legal troubles.

I have allowed myself to accept Hannah and Jack's love. I still think about my mom from time to time. Maybe she did love me in her own way. For she gave me to Hannah and Jack so they could provide me a life that she never could. There was something about that night in jail that changed me. It was the catalyst that started my journey back home, and I now wonder – did I really buy a ticket for Myrtle Beach?

Lynn's Thoughts …

Kristine's short story should be a must read for every young girl or woman. How many times must we relive this tale with basically the same results? Why can't the young see what they have, only to return years later to confront the truth … that love was where they started.

The birth mother in this little tale continues to haunt the girl throughout her life. And it was not until she accepted her mother's death that her life actually began. Children often blame themselves for their parent's failures. That blame then places the child into toxic relationships or situations … usually because the child believes that is all they deserve.

When the foster parents stood in the sunlight just waiting … my heart melted. Kristine did a wonderful job capturing what happens when self-realization hits … when truth passes into our reality.

Timothy's Birth Day

Mary Bendickson

It was still raining, and of course, it was a weekend. I was inside on the first week of spring, watching the snow melt and the rain drizzle. I wished I could take a walk in the sunshine. Maybe enjoy the brave crocus poking their purple pates above the white caps.

Oh, wait.

I couldn't walk much anymore. A knee injury a year ago.

Oh, wow!

Exactly, a year ago today. It was my grandson's first wedding anniversary. I had injured my knee when I tried to dance at his wedding. Shuffled around the floor with each of my sons, a son-law, and two … no three … of my grandsons. Instead of frolicking in the sun or dancing in the rain, I now find myself sitting here reminiscing.

This week marked Timothy's birthday. I thought of him a lot these days. Beating all odds, he would turn thirty-four.

Yes, thirty-four!

Everyone turned thirty-four, right? Not really a milestone. But for Timothy, it was something amazing. You see, he was a sort of miracle. Not an immaculate conception, but a miracle all the same. Maybe I should just start from the beginning … some thirty-four years ago …

– the rain – a steady, cold backdrop now –

My four children were raised in a broken home. A home I broke because I couldn't tolerate my high-school sweetheart husband sleeping with his police officer partner. I know, I know, terribly insensitive of me. I issued an ultimatum to choose between her or his family. He chose her, which left our children without a firm foundation and floundering in their teen years. They not only lost their once attentive dad, but their stay-at-home mom who now had to work. They were on their own until bedtime. Lots of time for mischief. However, my children are now amazing, God-fearing adults serving their families. But, we had a few rough times. Maybe the roughest involved Timothy.

– storm clouds are brewing –

My daughter had made a friend who lived not far from my work. She would often ask to spend the evening there while I worked. I did mention that my ex-husband never made an effort to spend time with his kids, right? Therefore, I was shocked when my daughter asked to spend the night at his place. Imagine my surprise when I discovered he didn't bother to take her to school the next day. The truth was that her father had taken her to an abortion clinic to confirm her suspicion that she was pregnant.

Pregnant! What? Where? When? How? Who?

– I can hear thunder rolling far away –

Dear old Dad thought he was doing me a favor by taking her to the clinic. He probably would have forced her into a solution had she not been too far along. In his benevolence, he took those first difficult steps, sparing me from ever knowing the truth. Alas, it turned out impossible to hide, and it was now my problem. He left me with the name of another clinic that would perform late-term abortions, and he probably figured he had done his due diligence.

My daughter was pregnant. Baggy clothes were in fashion and therefore no one suspected a thing. The *where* was … of course … her friend's house.

The when?

One of those hot summer nights.

The who?

The girlfriend had a sixteen-year-old brother.

The how

… well, you know that part.

The boy desperately wanted her to have an abortion, so I made him go with us. If she was to experience this, then he would too. I wanted both to hear exactly what would happen to this little life they had created.

– the sky has blackened –

We were informed that the pregnancy had progressed too far. But there was another place that could … I put my foot down. Nope, they were going to be parents, prepare for reality kids. I never saw such relief on my daughter's face. I knew she didn't want to kill her baby.

– the thunder is booming, the rain is drumming,

a whole symphony upon the roof –

Over the next few months, she studied with a tutor so she didn't have to attend classes. She had regular doctor visits. The projected due date was close. Her OBGYN took a vacation but asked us to come in for stress tests every other day while she was gone. No explanation given. It had been twelve years since I had a baby, perhaps procedures had changed. Besides, my daughter was young. Maybe, they're just playing it safe. But by all guesstimates, she was ten months – and huge.

The doctor ordered another ultrasound – she had returned from vacation. The technician asked us to wait while she consulted with the doctor.

First clue.

The doctor arrived and confirmed there was a problem. And … she didn't feel qualified to handle it. The head was enlarged … probable brain damage.

That's all?

TIMOTHY'S BIRTH DAY

– the deluge started –

Will it last a few minutes, a few hours, a few days, or weeks? Only the weatherman knows for sure, but he can't say. His is the only occupation you can get wrong 50% of the time and keep your job.

The next morning we arrived at the hospital. We wanted the father of the baby with us, but he was nowhere to be found. Doctors surrounded my little girl and started a barrage of tests. It was the first time I actually saw her huge baby bump for myself ... with an extra hump for the head. She was discreet. They presented us with a few options. We could kill the deformed baby in-uterus ... deliver it naturally ... have a C-section ... assist the fetus ... we opted for an immediate C-section and help with the baby.

Duh!

Little Timothy, all eleven pounds and a few ounces, was seizing at birth. The experts couldn't say if he would live for a few minutes, hours, days, weeks, or years. Where the brain should have been, only empty space – hydrocephalus meant water on the brain. Hydranencephaly meant no brain. Of course, the hospital was devoid of neurologists that day. The doctors ordered me and the baby to the next largest city to be examined.

Timmy, not me.

An MRI confirmed – no brain. Timmy was admitted into the NICU next to the teeny-tiny babies.

– there will be puddles to hurdle –

At some point Timmy's father arrived, but it was clear he didn't want a baby – he definitely didn't want a defective baby. His mother offered to help in any way possible, but unfortunately no way possible was found.

My daughter re-enrolled in her freshman high-school classes. She attended school while I watched the baby. I slept when she was home and worked the overnight shift. The boys were raising themselves at this point. My daughter had turned fifteen two months after Timothy's birth.

Timmy did a spot-on impersonation of Tweety-Bird. He was equipped with a shunt to drain excess water from the head. Social workers followed his progress, but it was evident he would not fit into their existing programs. They warned us he would have to be institutionalized and that his life span would be short. It would probably take a long time to find an opening in a residential setting. Therefore, we better start applying.

– a storm doesn't last forever –

We found a potential home for disabled children that was only an hour away. When they had an opening, they offered it to Timmy. It felt like Christmas. Probably, because it was Christmas. Timmy was the youngest resident at only nine months and was given the starring role as baby Jesus in their holiday play.

A feeding tube was placed in Timmy's stomach. Doctors determined he didn't have the reflexes required to suck properly. Besides, no one at the home had the time to get the job done. Years later, he developed other difficulties and another tube was necessary. Timmy-Two-Tubes was his nickname as he was wheeled around sporting two poles with attachments.

Timothy was a quadriplegic. Experts said he was blind and there was no connection from his ears to anything that would allow him to hear. And yet he responded exuberantly whenever he heard his name. A video, *'Timothy, The Littlest Angel,'* was his favorite. One Christmas, we visited a church that had a pipe organ. He was sound asleep but woke and smiled when it played. That convinced me he at least could *feel* vibrations. Therefore, we insisted the staff play loud classical music for him.

Just feel the beat.

Anytime we hugged or touched him, he rewarded us with the biggest, tooth-baring smile.

– must suffer the rain to have a rainbow,

God's own promise of better times –

Timothy survived numerous hospital stays. At age ten, a rod was placed in his back to keep him upright in his wheelchair. They replaced his tubing as he grew. He had respiratory problems and eventually, they placed him on a C-PAP machine. Sometimes he slept in an oxygen tent. He had COVID, and the restrictions were extreme, taking away touch – the only language Timothy understood. Timothy persevered through it all. We signed a do not resuscitate order. A hard decision to make.

– just as the rain brings blessings to the earth,
the sun will surely shine again –

How does one count a severely disabled baby a blessing to a barely grown little girl? That daughter of mine became a woman too fast, but she was an amazing one. She took charge and made all the decisions for Timothy's care. Just a few years ago, he was transferred to an adult home. We visited frequently. She became a mentor to other young girls experiencing unplanned pregnancies, proving there was hope and other options rather than abortions.

Even though she tried to work things out with Timothy's father, it didn't last. Instead, she married an extremely supportive man who was everything a husband and a father should be. She became the mother of four. She raised them home-schooled, and they are awesome. Her eldest daughter recently made me a great-grandmother.

Finding the good through the rain had been a rewarding adventure.

Let's live a little, Timothy!

I plan on visiting you on your birthday and, if you'll allow me to use your wheelchair as my walker, we'll explore the grounds, searching for daffodils and smelling the sweet cherry blossoms. Happy Birthday, may God continue to bless and keep you always.

Love, Grandma

Lynn's Thoughts …

Such a sad and wonderful story at the same time. The ethical and spiritual questions behind such a tale can become quite deep. The love we have for another often blinds us to the acceptance of what their life should or should not be.

Canada recently passed a Medical Assistance in Dying (MAID) law, which allows anyone, including children, the right to die by suicide. March 2024 is the date when children suffering from mental illness can receive assistance without parental consent. Would someone please define *mental illness*, because I believe that at times, we all fit into that category … I think we call them *Karens*?

Mary's heartwarming story about a child born to less than a perfect body makes us contemplate the real meaning behind life. Why are we here? Were we born just to be successful and if yes, would someone please define *success*?

If there is a soul in each body, then doesn't that soul have a right to live? And at what point is another given the power of the most holy to release that spirit? Perhaps *that* should be question.

Taking care of another can be draining on resources and time and emotions. However, perhaps that is why that individual entered our life in the first place. For us to learn how to care and nurture. Something that our spirit was assigned before birth.

A Tumbleweed and a Story

Page 7

Jonathan Michael Stroh

Jon Michael writes short and long stories while he studies creative writing and a few other things at Duke University. He is not the recipient of a MacArthur Fellowship but enjoys telling stories about how bizarre everything is. Opie and he will forever be a Midwesterner living in North Carolina.

Anaïssa Ali

ASPIC

Page 21

A free spirit in a healthy body . . .

Born in Mayotte, an island in the Indian Ocean, Anaïssa's father's military career took her to France. She studied chemistry in Germany before moving to Croatia with her son for the quality of life. She enjoys martial arts, good food, and traveling.

It is only in the last few years that she's discovered a passion for writing, especially short stories and poems that reflect her personal experiences, and the feelings they arouse in her. Anaïssa has an affinity for foreign languages, translating and writing novels in French, German, and English, collaborating with souls who have a story to tell.

Beyond her free spirit, she's an advocate of healthy living, hence her mission behind the name *The Mindfulspoon.* As a Certified Nutritionist, she assist others in developing healthy eating habits.

https://themindfulspoon.com

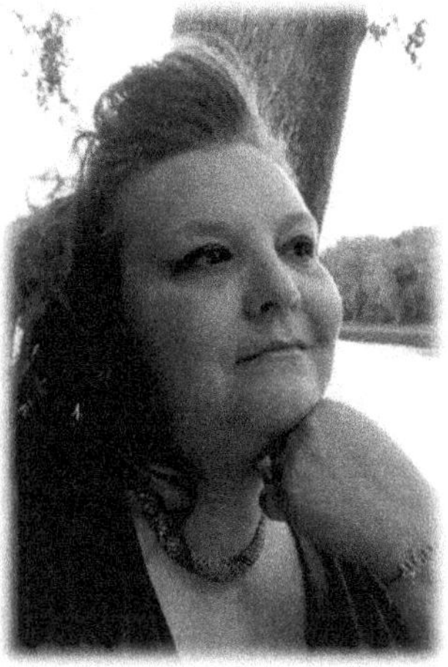

Beautiful Wreckage

Page 27

Valerie Dawn

Valerie, author of *End of The Rainbow, A Memoir of a Mother's Journey* spent her youth writing in secret. When she isn't enjoying nature with her family, she can be found with a book in her hands. Valerie is a social justice warrior advocating for changes. She wants to prove that although life is busy, there's no better time to support, educate, raise awareness, and challenge others to think outside the box. She continues to write utilizing the knowledge she's learned from her research and experiences.

https://authorvaleriedawn.com

Elizabeth Elder

Birds

Page 39

Elizabeth has written stories since she was seven and sees no reason to stop. Spending years in the nonfiction realm, she worked as a correspondent for various newspapers, and eventually, as editor for three weeklies in Maine. Elizabeth now lives in Putnam County, New York, renovating a little, old house and listening to the chatter of a few hundred birds.

D.M. Clemens

Bridge

Page 45

Daniela is a graphic designer and the co-founder of a tech company. She's fluent in Italian, has a bachelors in fine art, writes songs, fronted a garage band in San Francisco (like everyone else in the 90's) and illustrated a picture book about cheese addiction. She's the mother of three teenagers ruined by the internet and two eccentric cats. She recently finished a speculative fiction novel and is currently working on a short story series, as well as a new novel about a fictional town in Colorado. She writes when she should be parenting.

More of her stories can be found at dmclemens.com

Eden's Rain

Page 57

Samuel G. Tooma

Samuel worked as a Civilian Physical Oceanographer, spending time on the Arctic Ocean. He has over six papers in various scientific and trade journals. His work includes studies on the ocean environment, seafloor properties, and use of aircraft and satellite mounted remote sensors. All his studies were applied to the environmental impact on navy systems and operations.

In 2021, his debut novel, *The SOOF*, was published, and the sequel, *Assassin's Revenge,* in 2003.

www.samuelgtooma.com

Gears and Flowers

Page 77

Tai An Zhou

Tai An has worn many hats in his life – translator, poet, cosplayer, singer, part-time wizard, and lover of all things wonderful and strange. He's published in a national newspaper with a wide body of work online in a variety of genres.

http://www.tomato-of-justice.com

Getting Out

Page 91

Bruce Neuburger

Bruce is a former farm and factory worker and cab driver, ESL, and video arts teacher. He is now retired.

Author of *Lettuce Wars: Ten Years of Work and Struggle in the Fields of California* published by Monthly Review Press and the Spanish translation Guerras de Lechuga published by Köehler Books.

Author of articles on social justice issues, especially immigrants.

Light

Page 107

Jerry Aveta

Jerry graduated with a bachelor's in Electrical Engineering from Virginia Military Institute (VMI). He was awarded by the Secretary of the Army the Distinguished Civilian Service award.

Jerry's career included teaching, counseling, and pastoring in various communities of faith for over thirty years. He has served in various capacities in denominational and non-denominational churches where he developed a view unique and relevant for our times. *The Evidence of Things Unseen* was published in 2021, with *Faith for the Times* in 2023.

https://faithforthetimes.net

BIOGRAPHIES

Onyx Rebel

It Was Worth It

Page 123

Chase has always been a lover of books, the feeling of escape into the unknown. It wasn't until she was in high school that her desire to become an author hit. She now writes poetry and nonfiction, and is currently working on her first novel.

Morna Gersho

Knitting in the Dark

Page 131

After spending 25 very rewarding years in the classroom teaching third graders, Morna now devotes her time to writing. When not honing her craft with online classes at Storyteller's Academy or writing on her blog, she is learning from Society of Children's Book Writers or several critique groups. She has also participated in various online picture book writing challenges and workshops. She holds a teaching credential, a bachelor's in drama, and an master's in British literature. She is a self-confessed bibliophile.

BIOGRAPHIES

Last Legs

Page 139

Kevin Hopson

Kevin has dabbled in many genres over the years. A few of his stories have won various contests, and his work has appeared in more than twenty anthologies. You can learn more about Kevin by visiting his website.

http://www.kmhopson.com.

Thomas Bell

Mama Luisa

Page 145

Born and raised in Arizona, Thomas enjoys a love affair with the southwest and Mexico. He has written a series of books that take place in Mexico during the 1890's. When he's not counseling, writing, or loving his family, he can be found in a back alley searching for the best *street* tacos.

Roger L. Guffey

Rainy Day Memories

Page 159

Roger is a retired high school teacher. In addition to writing short fiction, he's a regular contributor to the Op-Ed section of the local newspaper with columns dealing with social, political, and educational issues.

In addition to writing, Roger is an award winning photographer and an accomplished gardener. His love of mathematics and photography culminated in his publishing a coffee table book, *Mathematical Curves of the Bluegrass* that uses photographs of the Kentucky horse farms to illustrate mathematical concepts and equations.

He shares his home with six cats: two Maine Coon, a Himalayan, a European Burmese and two domestic short hairs. As an active member of a Presbyterian Church, he often infuses spiritual aspects into his short stories as meditative themes to explore the spiritual side of life.

BIOGRAPHIES

Shy Boy

Page 167

Frank Shima

Frank Shima, a native of Minnesota, either entertains or annoys his neighbors by playing Czech songs on his accordion. He has written four novels, *Vencil*, *Dead Letter*, *Plum Creek*, and *Lying in the Weeds*. His plays have been performed throughout the United States including Alabama, California, Florida, Georgia, Long Island, Louisiana, Massachusetts, Minnesota, North Carolina, and Ohio, as well as England and Wales, which is where he learned not to use unleaded gas in a diesel engine.

Spiraling

Page 177

Tia Shanklin

Tia Shanklin is a recent English and creative writing graduate of Ashland University in Ashland, Ohio. She's continuing with her master's in creative writing. This is her first piece for publication.

The Glitch

Page 185

Arthur Doweyko

Arthur is an award-winning writer whose favorite genres include science fiction and fantasy. His novels *Algorithm*, published in 2014, and *As Wings Unfurl* in 2021, are available on Amazon. His anthology, *Captain Arnold,* garnered the 2021 Royal Palm Literary Award (*2nd Runner up*).

Arthur is a scientist with many papers and patents, include 3D drug design software. His life-long interest in science heavily influences his writings and paintings.

Arthur won the 2022 L. Ron Hubbard Achievement Award for illustrators. His illustrations have graced the covers of various books.

http://www.ArthurMDoweyko.com

The Prodigal Cousin

Page 205

Gary Girzadas

Gary is a first-time author. However, he is no stranger to writing and has self-published on topics ranging from music to politics. He is known to love a good book club conversation. Gary navigates the world of higher education and wrangles grants for various projects. A native of Chicagoland, Gary now resides with his wife and four children in beautiful Skaneateles, New York.

Lady Beth

The Puddle and The Ghost

Page 221

Beth was born and raised in Wisconsin, and moved to Virginia to pursue a degree in aeronautical engineering management. She fell in love with the area, along with an amazing job keeping the world a little safer. Currently, she's working on a master's degree in homeland security and emergency management. Her hobbies include working on a pilot's license, camping, and enjoying the company of her dog. However, she'll always be a Wisconsin girl in a Virginia world.

The Undead FriendZone

Page 233

Tyler Tarter

Tyler's writing career began in 2020. He enjoys exploring various genres and has loyal fans who eagerly await his latest releases.

With a focus on technology, Tyler creates new ideas and technological twists on magical systems.

He studied martial arts, which gives him a unique perspective on combat and ancient warfare.

https://www.tylertarter.com

Ticket to Abbeville

Page 245

Kristine K. McCraw

Kristine started writing as a hobby that quickly became an escape. Now, she doesn't want to stop. As a veteran teacher of almost thirty years, her love of stories started with children's books, maturing into adult fiction. She published *The Spirit of Sunflowers* in 2021 and is working on her second novel, *Beautiful Dreamer*. She shares her thoughts and ideas on her personal blog. Kristine will be retiring from teaching in 2024 and plans to continue her journey in writing.

https://www.kconnection.blog

Timothy's Birth Day

Page 257

Mary Bendickson

Mary has always enjoyed reading but found little time once married. For nine years, she raised four children as a single mother while running her own business. She remarried, following her new husband throughout the U.S. with his career. After taking up reading as a main hobby and consuming many romance novels, she wondered if she had it in her to write creatively.

In August 2023, Mary won *The Claymore Award* for best western genre at the Killer Nashville Writers Conference for the first fifty pages of her unpublished manuscript.

Lynn Yvonne Moon

Growing Up Aspie

Page 3

Lynn is an award-winning author of adult, young adult, and children literature with over ten books in print. She holds a master's in public administration from Troy State University and a master's in literature from Lindenwood University.

Printed in the USA
CPSIA information can be obtained
at www.ICGtesting.com
LVHW090958171223
766701LV00023B/166/J

9 781953 278487